TALKING TO MY WALL
DURING COVID-19
ISOLATION

Collection of Narrative Essays
by glyn dowden

Interior formatting and cover design:
Moore Media, Inc., Plymouth, MA
moore-media-inc.com

ISBN: 978-0-578-30434-2

Printed in the United States of America.

First Edition

For Jacob

Contents

Acknowledgements

I thank John Poignand for his support and contribution to this collection of essays. To the many fellow writers from the Sandwich Arts Alliance and 4 CCs, all of whom, knowingly or not, assisted me in writing this book through the process of critique, I offer my profound thanks to all of them. I also thank my wonderful wife, Magdalen, for her encouragement and unstinting advice.

Lastly, but not least, I thank Moore Media for preparing and laying out this book for publication.

Essays originally contributed by John Poignand:

- Gratitude
- Purple and More
- The Virus
- Clock Is Ticking

TALKING TO MY WALL DURING COVID-19 ISOLATION

What's This All About?

This document is a receptacle, a treasure chest, a garbage
can, a coffin for words and ideas and suchlike that spill
out of one's head without much thought or restraint. Stuff
that needs or doesn't need to be said and maybe a rant
or two, but mostly reflections of the simple mysteries
impinging on our lives. Woe is the person who chooses not
to acknowledge that because they have yet to understand;
at the end of the day, life has nothing and everything to
do with them. And now, during this historic period, is the
chance to say something, anything, in order to stake a small
claim on planet Earth—hosting Covid-19.

When facing a pandemic and destabilization, this is that
special moment. The moment when you make your voice
heard using a good dose of fatalistic cynicism, along with
irrational optimism. That is, when you mull over questions
that spring to the surface, such as: why do some strangers
scare me while others don't, why does the cat sometimes
behave as if she can see things I cannot see, why are some
people attracted to each other for life, do people die of
a broken heart, what replaces religion, why do we keep
exploring and gathering, why are we unsatisfied, does the
wall capture my words, how many times will I say "What the
fuck," during my lifetime? Will isolation have side benefits
like only changing socks once a week, or do you rediscover
bingo, stamp collecting, and so many other exciting
unknowns?

Ducking for Cover

I'm telling you, the first time I took it seriously was when Doreen came tearing up from the basement where she had been putting clothes in the dryer.

"I just heard," she said. Actually, she sounded a little hysterical. "We are going to have to take extreme measures," she said. "That is, we have to isolate ourselves. Only leaving the house, when absolutely necessary, with a mask, gloves, and glasses. We are going to have to disinfect everything and keep washing our hands. And if we don't, they said there's a good chance we'll die from Covid. You know that virus Trump reckoned was no different than the flu."

She had come bounding into the kitchen and started giving me instructions.

"Cliff, please wash your hands, put on your boots, stick this over your face; we're going to the bank and Stop and Shop. Quick, get a move on before everyone else empties the shelves."

"Wait a minute," I said. "Trump's telling us it's no problem, and he's not wearing a mask. He's going to drink Clorox and swallow a small light bulb, or something like that," I said with a smirk on my face.

"What the hell are you on about? Why are you listening to that fool? I've told you before not to watch that damn TV station. Now shift yourself," she said.

We swung into the parking lot, and Doreen was out and running before I had switched off the engine. I caught up to her in the third aisle.

"They've run out of toilet paper and ice cream," she said. "There are only four cans of baked beans left. No, don't take just one; take them all. What? I don't care about someone else. Bread, where's the bread?"

2

Even with the mask, Doreen's face had a kinda wild look. It was in her eyes, and I don't think she had bothered to comb her hair.

She strode off, pushing the cart before her, following large red arrows stuck on the floor into the next aisle. Butter, take half a dozen, sausages you always like sausages, four dozen eggs that's good, and so it went on until we had what I thought was two weeks supply. Mostly of food that was available, some of which we don't normally eat. But hey, this is war; when you have to stock up, and you can't get enough. I recalled my mother telling me about the World War, ration books, and food shortages. Well, Doreen wasn't going to let that happen to us.

"When will you have toilet rolls?" I asked the cashier; she checked the date then a schedule next to her register.

"Not for another ten days, if we're lucky. We open at seven. Get here early," she said through her mask.

I turned to Doreen and said, "Don't worry, I used newspaper to wipe my arse fifty years ago, I can do it again."

Doreen, bless her, always has a positive attitude. But she didn't fancy newsprint on the cheeks of her bum.

"Okay, fine," she said. "You use the Cape Cod Times, and I'll use toilet paper. Cliff, I forgot the Coke. Just go and get six bottles of Coke while she's checking me out," Doreen said.

"We're out of Coke," the girl said.

"What? Out of Coke? Unbelievable! I've never heard of such a thing!" Doreen yelled.

"Yea, they cleared that off the shelves by ten o'clock this morning," the girl mumbled with a shrug of her shoulders.

"Jesus Doreen," I said. "We need to get over to the liquor store right now. God forbid that they should run out of booze."

It's almost the end of the month now, daffodils are coming out, but we stay indoors unless we have no alternative but to go outside dressed like bandits. The TV says this could go on until sometime next year and I inform Doreen that Trump is going to hold a big rally somewhere down South. He won't wear a mask, and neither will most of the crowd.

"That shows you; it can't be serious," I say with a half-smile on my face.

She responded, "Just you wait, in a couple of weeks most of those people will come down with Covid, and no, I don't want to know what Giuliani is saying. He's crazy. Have you seen his eyes? While we're at it, why don't you get your head out of that TV and make a start on the garden?"

"By the way, Cliff, did I see you talking to Carol at the end of the driveway?" she asked.

"Yeah, her grandson has come down with Covid," I said.

"What? And you were out there talking to her for about ten minutes? Do you know what six feet apart is? And also by the way, you weren't wearing a mask. I was damn well horrified," she yelled.

"Carol's all right," I said. "You can trust her."

Doreen stared at me for a long time, probably wondering whether I understood the words *pandemic* and *isolation*.

"Cliff, why don't you make a start on those jigsaw puzzles you got for Christmas? This is going to be hard work keeping you locked down. How our marriage is going to survive during the many months ahead is going to be interesting," she said.

"Doreen, it's the Thursday Special at The Post House tonight. They've put heaters out on the deck. What do you think?" I asked hopefully.

I think I heard her say something like, "Jesus Christ!"

4

Beware the Ides of March

Walls and windows, windows and walls, there's no escape. What can I say?

You know, ever since the announcement, crocuses and daffodils have been close to full bloom. They don't know we've been officially warned—Covid cometh! Isolate, stay at home, hide in the kitchen, bake bread, do something, stock toilet rolls, wash your hands.

I have to ask you what will it all lead to, what's it going to be, extinction or isolation?

There was no reply from the wall.

The other night, I was watching something on TV. NOVA, I think. Scientists were on about the last extinction a couple of hundred million years ago. Of course, Trumpsters tell us not to believe a word they say, and that's all right with me, especially when they get the bloody weather forecast wrong, and I leave my umbrella at home. Anyway, the boffins reckon that there have been multiple extinctions due to this and that over an unimaginable time. But not only that, the swines further upset me by babbling on, saying we could be approaching another one.

What on earth does that mean? I guess we are always approaching something: death, winter, hell, traffic lights, toothache, the next extinction. You name it; we're going there.

Who are they to keep scaring me? That's what I want to know. And stop testing. That's what Humpty Dumpty in the Whitehouse says, and he has a point. Kick science up the bum, that's what he says, and he should know; he's been doing it long enough. Mind you; the greatest thrill would be watching my Doreen kick him in the you-know-whats.

So, this extinction thing. What are we going to do about it? Of course, in the past, it was never complete extinction. Some buggers survived, such as a few plants, bugs, a couple of fish, and several ugly animals with large teeth. Viola— from those setbacks, we emerged, and our brain grew faster than all other species. At least that's what I am told.

It all sounds a bit sketchy to me, don't you think?

Mind you, here we are talking about millions and millions of years. I can't imagine! Let's face it; next week is a long time for Doreen. I said to her, "Look, if you don't believe the egg-heads, you can always resort to the religious stuff. You know, creationism something like that—the odd gathering, confession, and sacrifice while singing *We're all going to heaven in a big blue bus*. But first, make sure someone has a guitar."

But what I'm wondering is, why did God only turn up after the sixth extinction? Was he busy somewhere else? Was Gabriel impregnating someone else? Of course, I realize, God works in mysterious ways and may not have noticed those nasty inquisitions and evangelical sods here in America who set about murdering the locals and lynching black people while playing on the pipe organ: *We'll get to paradise first, so screw you.*

Oh, look at that, a few sparrows have come to visit.

Anyway, as we forge ahead, ignoring the doomsayers, destroying most species, and creating climate change, I have to wonder what our next trick will be after this pandemic has passed. Maybe Trump is the new John the Baptist? We'll have his head eventually, but who will come in his wake? That's the scary part. By the way, did you know that Londoners used to ice skate on the river Thames during Brueghel's time?

This climate forecasting is all a bit sort of pie-in-the-sky stuff. Although best to be safe than sorry, that's what I say, and I always keep a thermos flask filled with tea, a pork pie, wooly socks, and spare pair of galoshes handy.

Also, I must remember: When wearing a mask, if some fat guy with a pineapple head, two crooked front teeth, pot belly, dressed in ridiculous camouflage, gives me the finger and preaches the gospel according to anger, hate, and abuse: the Mark, Luke, and John version of the Holy Word, to take no notice. Go home and pour a chocolate martini.

Will my Doreen and I be here when the world rights itself? That's a good question.

Did I mention the daffodils?

Should we all commit hara-kiri after the next election? Because no matter who wins, it's clear that giving everyone a gun and a say in what should be done is not the most constructive way to save the world. What do we want—the Constitution for dreamers or extinction?

Forget it; we won't have a vote on this one; it's going to be extinction. That is, according to my next door neighbor, Shirley, who's a gynecologist, or is it a chiropodist? Whatever, she's an expert.

So tell me. What do you think?

Go on, tell me.

Covid and Isolation

I thought about this gadget I'm using; that is, my computer, and said to myself, *This is like an umbilical cord transferring my thoughts and speech to a screen through my fingers.*

Are you taking it all in, or are you like some kind of sounding board? What the hell? Who knows what goes on when there is no one to interface with except Doreen. And let's be honest, she doesn't want to hear me rambling on.

This could be it; me, the computer, and you the wall. People reckon they can sometimes hear voices in the walls of old houses. Will you capture my voice? Will you speak one day?

Actually, I sometimes wonder what happens to words once they are flung into the air as sound bites. Do the sound waves just dissipate, or cling together and somehow float off, or bury themselves? Will they come back, as the saying goes, to haunt us? Will they be picked up randomly out of the atmosphere and used by someone?

Of course, this sort of thinking is only remotely relevant if one believes in the individual uniqueness of this world. And I, of course, do not, and therefore this rambling hypothesis I'm on at the moment is just a load of bollocks, possibly caused by an untethered brain with little to do except rummage around in isolation.

I remember many years ago visiting the Smithsonian Planetarium. I, laying on my back, gazing up into the heavens and becoming overwhelmed by the wonder, the grandeur, the magnificence of this mysterious creation moving away from me. It was as though, for the first time, I realized just how tiny we are and how short a lifetime we have. It's astonishing how blindingly brief our lives are, and even the insignificant existence of the whole human race is, when compared to the depth and breadth of space.

In fact, our time is so brief that on a universal level, it must be like the splutter of a candle or the intake of a breath. And now, as I come closer to the end of this experience called life, as my body creaks like a stem bending and twisted petals falling at the end of winter, it is with humility that I'm presenting these thoughts, images, and expressions or whatever they are. Call them what you will, but let them reveal that which lies deep within. That mystery roiling in your head; what am I, and why? And let us assume we know nothing about these matters only that as far as we can tell, it is now, and we are here.

Today we are engulfed in the fury of a pandemic caused by a deadly virus. A moment in history when the whole human race has to protect itself from the unseen. A force that is not made by us or exists through our choosing. A pandemic that leaves us little choice but to withdraw from society and slowly lose the sense of connection, confidence, and purpose. Will we gradually disappear?

Is it only with hope that we face tomorrow?

No! I vehemently say. *No, April brings us tulips, magnolias, and renewal. And we must all hang out while apart, share thoughts, hypotheses, rant, and rave. We have a long road ahead. Sign-up for this and for that, make a noise; it's isolation, not extinction,* I say, just before putting my mask, gloves, and glasses on and furtively looking up and down the road, before I step out of the house.

Entering the Wilderness

What do you think? I'm thinking about isolation in America, here in Cape Cod, and wondering whether it means the same thing for people in other countries and whether it is different from how we would have behaved in the past.

I'm also thinking, one of America's unique features in the modern era is the distance and separation of families. America is the size of a continent, and even though some say it is a melting pot, it has, I suppose you might say, a homogenous culture.

That is, the same language and general behavior and such, across the land. This then makes migration from one coast, state, city, town, or job to another quite easy.

Thus when children go to college, they often end up far away and then settle down elsewhere, somewhat estranged from parents and siblings. It is not an unnatural situation for them because the previous generation had done the same thing when they were children. Therefore aunties, uncles, cousins, and grandparents are mostly somewhere else, not upstairs in the third bedroom, on the toilet, next door, or around the corner.

I'm guessing that this demographical behavior in America probably accelerated around the 1950s early '60s when colleges became easily accessible and U-Haul had more than 10,000 trailers on the road. But not so much for the lower working class and poor immigrant families. And not so much in most parts of Europe where families continue to live close to each other, often in multi-generational houses. That is, those families and school friends' bonds, under those circumstances, are more robust, the dependence more profound.

Talking about American colleges, notwithstanding the outrageous cost of education, they are so prolific that you have to be pretty dumb not to qualify for some sort of college education. Mind you, the average non-academic smart kid—goes to a trade school and ends up running his or her own business, has a house, truck, a boat, skis in Vermont, and marries a nurse or teacher to cover medical benefits extortion.

And so, getting back to the point—for Americans, the outcome of the isolation or forced separation from family is probably less dramatic. I suppose you can add to that the fact that technology and the over-protection of children have resulted in them being less involved in face-to-face activities like hanging out from morning to dusk in the street.

When considering this, you would think it further supports the probability that Americans can handle isolation better than most. And yet, guess again; the infection rate from Covid-19 in America is one of the world's worst. Go figure that one out.

Blame those blasted Trumpsters who walk around without a mask; that's what I say. Mind you, not surprisingly, that's my default position for most of what goes wrong around here—blame Trump.

Actually, a place like Cape Cod is an excellent example of this. It is a place similar to Florida, where people choose to get away from their kids. It is a place to die, where seeing grandchildren and children is not a spontaneous event but something that happens four or five times a year. We are no longer in a society where one can say, oh, let's pop around grandma's, or see uncle George in the pub, or visit cousin Dora's house. I was told they are closing schools on the Cape for lack of customers.

It seems to me, even though we would wish otherwise, the fact is, most of our grandchildren have little experience of knowing and forming a deep relationship with grandparents. Family dynamics, except perhaps for the poor and the rich, have changed. So for those of a certain age, this isolation has pushed us further adrift. Joining groups, sharing thoughts, connecting and expanding interests, sowing friendships, even if it's only through Zoom, is probably vital for our wellbeing.

Of course, it's just a thought; I could be wrong. Maybe there's a poem in all of this.

On the Other Hand

On the other hand, someone I know, named Linda, said that separating families ensures vitality and allows, or rather necessitates, extreme creativity. This, she said, accounts for the unlimited opportunities for wealth, risk, scientific, academic, and artistic innovation.

Families glued together, ever watched over by generational owls, tend to remain more insular and static. The supposition being, she said, you can't have one without the other. She carried on by saying, you have to accept that growth is painful, and many fall through the cracks as they leap from the nest. Easy for her to say.

It is an interesting observation and probably wrong. In fact, data would suggest that, by and large, there have been great strides of improvement in people's lives over the past hundred or so years. Poverty and starvation have been reduced. Democracy and the voice of freedom have also painstakingly expanded across the world, and life expectations have improved, except in America. History has shown that people's movement and the sharing of ideas have made life better, not worse, and that isolationism does not promote or energize change.

But for many, the extraordinary advances in my lifetime have come at a high price and could present danger for the world itself. Why? Because the overwhelming objective should have been and should continue to be that of happiness.

Happiness for everyone should be the goal, but the world's leading country, irrespective of its advancements, does not seem to be making much headway in that regard. In fact, within the happiness league and based upon so many other 'social progress' measurements, the U.S. is placed well below other advanced countries.

For instance: having your son become a successful doctor living in, say, Palo Alto; a daughter working on the stock exchange in New York; a parent in one of Florida's hideouts; and you in a tax haven such as New Hampshire, may in some small way spur-on the country's economical, technical advancement but offers nothing towards the enjoyment of bonding with family and friends, the transfer of love from one to another, the joy of walking in the shadows of your children's, children's children, that is, those who hardly know you. At the end of the day, you have to ask: what are changes and growth for, other than the advancement of happiness?

Perhaps the new generation will recognize those mistakes of the past and start to clean up the mess we have left behind in our quest for so-called growth. It seems clear to me that the strength of a society is not in the spaces, but in the common bonds that are established and maintained within that society.

Perhaps, this isolation will slightly change the way people act and behave towards their family and each other. After all, in the end, what's it all about? Of course, as I say, I could be wrong, and maybe a lot of people in the U.S. can't stand being with most of their family members.

Living with Slogans

My mother used to say, *It never rains, but it pours*, and let me tell you, that is no exaggeration in Wales. Another one of her sayings was, *Misery always comes in threes*.

I was thinking about that this morning and how appropriate it was for 2020. And no doubt, if you live in a lousy place where life is a continuous struggle from morning to night, then *three* may be a low misery number.

But for us here in the West, we don't expect to be struck down with the likes of Ebola, flooding, starvation, gangster governments, terrorists, bombs, and a Chinese virus. Here we expect life to continue predictably with manageable setbacks such as losing your job, divorce, recession, and having to forgo a vacation.

Certainly not this: a bloody maniac just elected as president with a cult-like far-right following, suppression and the killing by police of black people, along with the Covid-19 pandemic.

We thought we had it all covered. We'd worked out everything such that various issues and setbacks would never get out of hand, and if they did, then we had the controls and management in place to deal with the situation efficiently. How wrong was that?

Make America Great Again. People love simple slogans: *Contract with America, Take Back Control, Yes We Can, Government's Not the Answer—Government's the Problem,* and all the rest of the shitty, simplistic statements which have been promulgated far and wide as solutions. Meanwhile, here I am, talking to a wall, afraid to go out.

Of course, if you're black or brown, or in the lower working class, living near the shit heaps, one step away from living out of your car, you have no choice but to go out there amid Covid and face the music. Someone has to collect the garbage, deliver packages, clean up, man the hospitals, make the bread—no working from home for your lot. No digital miracle will rescue you. And I wonder will we ever prioritize the world from the bottom up rather than from the top down.

I was born at a time when you ran for cover, hoping a bomb wouldn't drop on your head. Just like those poor bastards in Syria and other places, and now, near the end of my life, I duck for cover, hoping a virus won't come my way.

Now we have a clown in charge who beats his chest, talks about America's space warriors and controlling space, and kicks the Chinese in the goolies. Well, I'm thinking best of luck with that, they make Apple computers, sneakers and buy our debt. At the same time, I'm thinking, why do I concern myself with such thoughts when I have to dress like a bank robber and keep my distance when going outside.

As if there weren't enough already, Americans are loading up on more guns, anxious to shoot someone, while the police seem to make a habit of shooting black people. Normally, I wouldn't think too much about this because it is the poor and, therefore, most especially black neighborhoods where street crime occurs. But, as I've been forced to reflect on the situation while looking out the window, as life goes by and cute squirrels dart around, I wonder why police shoot black people in the back, choke them and harass them: *your tail light is bust, you didn't signal, your sticker's out of date, do you live here*, and all that nonsense. I know the psychology; stop the small stuff turning into more significant crimes, but that's not the real story.

That just leads us to where we are now: overflowing jails, under-managed and under-resourced privatized prisons, and criminality within the jails. I'm thinking about my work colleague who went to prison for a white-collar crime, and for no reason at all, except he was French, ended up in a high-risk security prison. I have to believe his book, *The American Trap*, in which he describes the shocking account of what the experience was like. That is, I accept his presentation of what the real disgraceful privatized incarceration situation is like versus the statistics and statements coming out of our justice system.

And so we have *Black Lives Matter*, another slogan to get us off our backside. But I have to wonder, will it improve things in this country while we have such a massive discrepancy between the haves and have-nots—a gap that has now reached unparalleled proportions. I think not.

While hanging around at home, TV is a sanctuary with reruns of this and that, but I have to admit, I have all but stopped listening to the news, slogans, and American manufactured views.

Gratitude

In my morning haze, I gazed with a somewhat narcissistic curiosity at my reflection in the bathroom mirror. I'm shaving the results of a two-day beard while staring at my eyes that sometimes seem to have an answer to the question, *Who am I?*

The gurgle of water trickling into the sink, swirling soap down the drain, laughed at my question and I noticed that I had cut the edge of my chin—no electric razors for me. I rinsed, then dried my face, stemmed the blood, and took leave of my image, resolving not to bother it again.

There was a calm quietness at the breakfast table, a stillness that didn't have to be interrupted with questions and answers. In any event, what more was there to say? I'd been in virtual isolation for months.

The kettle's whistle pleaded for a cooler position on the stove and in its warped roundness, my face stared back at me.

Outside, a squirrel perching on his haunches cautiously peered at me through the window, its mouth full of raided birdseed. Whiskers twitching nervously under my scrutiny, he stayed put, enjoying the morning sunlight on his fur. Was it a he? I assumed it was a he, but I hadn't a clue.

The up-popping toast broke the spell and sent him scurrying. I returned to the toaster, buttered a slice of bread, and enjoyed the reflecting sun in a corner of the kitchen.

The clock chimed seven times, and its second hand continued on its way, around and around. Time tantalizingly moved slowly onward as I wait for the day when we can all freely walk outside without concern.

There was the smell of hot toast, the taste of melted butter, and the sound of me crunching just before I took a sip of coffee. My hand reached into my shirt pocket, feeling for the cigarette pack against my chest. Once again, I had gone back to smoking.

Outside, the wind lifted leaves. A robin hopped across the lawn, searching for worms. A wasp landed on the screen and crawled up to the wooden window ledge. A shiver ran down my back; my hand flicked the screen—the wasp buzzed in confusion and flew off. Blue cigarette smoke gathered in layers of sunlight, its tang mingling with the aroma of coffee.

I gathered up dishes and placed them in the sink and walked out onto the deck. The air was fresh and tasted cool. I could hear the soft coo of a mourning dove and distant hum of a car. It was that moment when my recluse world was still coming awake—the moment when the sun's glare, which was low on the horizon, made my eyes water. Doreen was still in bed. She wouldn't be up for an hour or so. *I think I'll go for a drive*, I murmured to myself.

The car growled to life, throbbing, ready to spring forward as the tachometer rose and fell. We, the Porsche and me, moved out into the street. Onto the uneven road, and within seconds, telephone poles and trees were sliding past as the car, and I headed up into the hills. The tall tree's shadows breaking the morning sunlight. The wind whistled by, and I laughed. Unrestrained; free for a short while.

We paused on the crest of the hill, and I stepped out of the car, shielded my eyes, and gazed across a valley of fields, hedgerows, small farmhouses, and winding lanes. Breathed in the morning air to clear my head's mild hangover, and then I could not help myself. In a raised voice, I shouted— *Thank you, God, I am still here!*

But now unfortunately, I'm back here, sitting in this chair talking to you.

Truth

"One of the great regrets of my presidency is that I didn't get him [bin Laden] for you, because I tried to," Clinton claimed. Bush told the 9/11 commission he was sure Clinton had mentioned terrorism but did not remember talking about al-Qaeda.

I don't know why Clinton felt the need to try and publicly forgive himself for not getting bin Laden and his cutthroats. It sounds like the excuse of a schoolboy: *please, sir, I did my best, sir*. When in fact, he did next to sweet nothing. After all, al-Qaeda wasn't exactly in super deep undercover. They were busy acquiring finance, recruiting and training people, and attacking U.S. locations and facilities.

But Clinton wasn't famous for telling the truth. Lying was part of his game, whether to his family, friends, under oath, or the public.

And so I sit here wondering about truth. Sometimes lying is thought to be necessary; for example, what people say may be for someone's own good. Perhaps those are the most common of lies. Starting with the small ones—*you're looking well, you look so young, I'm doing this for you, I love you*—and so the list goes on. They are the harmless white lies that help maintain harmony.

Then there are the more definitive lies—*I was not speeding, I did not run the dog over*. Followed up with *not guilty, I was never there*. Then the high-ranking lies, those found at government level. Those that deny torture, cause wars, have people killed, followed by the blatant corrosive political lies that sow discontent and perverts democracy.

I suppose this sort of lying has been going on forever; however, now the situation is different. In the past, when compared to today, communication was slow. But now, all public words of interest are conveyed around the world within minutes. Not only that, but the media is open to any group. You no longer have to be famous or own a newspaper or broadcasting station. Connection to the public can be instantly achieved using social media outlets with little or no fact-checking.

Now we have conspiracy theorists pretending what they say has merit or some element of truth. The sort of communication we are exposed to now has become the fastest and cheapest way to incite people, particularly those dissatisfied with their lives and those who want to blame others.

Unfortunately, this behavior needs little encouragement. When politicians, time and time again, are shown to have knowingly lied and, when exposed, walk away saying things like, *my words were taken out of context, you misunderstood, I was misinformed, I'll walk that back,* there is hardly any blowback, no culpability.

Today, when blatant lying is integrated with conspiracy theories and politics on mass media, it instantaneously enters the World Wide Web, and since the Constitution protects the freedom of speech in the U.S., this becomes a cocktail that when shaken, leads, just like a pandemic, to riotous behavior. Especially in a country such as America, where there are large ready-made pools of ignorance with guns.

And so I sit here within this room, beginning to understand that we are going through a sea of change that will require an overhaul of our free market system and regulations to protect all ethical standards and the Constitution. This I share with you for the record, knowing full well that even though lies have caused wars, injustice, and death in the past, we cannot dispel our modern-day concerns about truth and ignorance.

Purple and More

Sitting here clicking away on my computer, I notice the brilliant purple in one of the pictures on the wall, and that has got me thinking about color.

In school, Mr. Mogridge, the science teacher, when talking about different colors in the spectrum, would use a glass prism to separate light into its wavelengths, and we would see red, orange, yellow, green, blue, indigo, and violet.

However, later on, I learned there were more. Just outside our visual range, there is ultraviolet light and infrared light that scientists discovered in the early 1800s. More than a hundred years later, I learned about dark matter, the presence of which could only be inferred through its gravitational effects on our galaxy.

Not only that, but I have subsequently learned that on both sides of the light spectrum are wavelengths unseen by humans. Infrared on one side and ultraviolet on the other. So I have to wonder: if I were a butterfly, bird, insect, or another animal, what color range would I have?

I'm also wondering what effect color has on a person's psyche. Quite a lot, apparently. Did various artists know this throughout the ages? Did that go a long way towards one almost identical piece of art being considered superior to another? Does everyone see the same shade of color? Obviously not because at one end of the color perception is color blindness, which we are all aware of. But I wonder about the other end, what goes on there?

Are some people dazzled by the various hues and shades of multiple colors?

Why am I going on about colors, I ask myself, and realize it is the brilliant purple in one of my pictures that frequently draws my attention.

And this is what's so interesting. Purple has been the color most often associated with royalty, magic, mystery, and piety from way back. Moreover, when combined with pink, it is associated with sex.

In times gone by, making purple dye was a long, difficult, and expensive procedure. It was extracted from a sea snail. Thousands of tiny snails had to be found, each removed from their shell and soaked, then a tiny gland removed and placed in sunlight. The juice, over time, changed color. Mountains of empty shells have been found at the ancient sites of Sidon and Tyre.

As you can imagine, the supply of these tiny shells waned, and their price rose. Wearing clothes dyed in it became an indication of wealth and power. Soon royalty, cardinals, and popes fashioned their garments in purple. And, as it so happens, many of these characters were mildly insane, so purple became associated with madness.

Women of the night have long used purple to their advantage, knowing that purple coupled with pink increases the appearance of sensuality, eroticism, femininity, and seduction.

Was this the start of one of the biggest industries in the world? No, not prostitution, but I guess something somewhat related. That is, the pharmaceutical companies selling cosmetics made of snail shells and other stuff to women intent on attracting a mate.

It is amazing what I think of, or feed my brain with, when sitting here talking to you.

Kids Next Door

I heard kids in the garden next door playing hide and seek, and this got me remembering my childhood. Back then, where and when I grew up, things were very different.

The neighborhoods I knew were right next to, or within walking distance of fields with cows and horses, trees you could climb, ditches you could jump, and wild blackberries you could pick while making sure you didn't step in cow shit, or that the farmer, Dickie Walters, hadn't let his bull loose in the field.

When we weren't in the fields, we played in the streets, girls tending dolls, skipping and playing hopscotch, while boys played cowboys and Indians, football, cricket, and wrestled, from morning till night. No one wanted to go home for lunch or be called in at night for dinner.

Dealing with life, fights, the mystery of sex, its temptations and lure was figured out in the streets and fields, and like the plague you avoided, parents and those older siblings who would tell on you.

There was a time and season for everything: jackstones, conkers, roller skating, sports, hangman, fireworks, and egg hunting. The poor birds around our neighborhood didn't stand a chance. As soon as their nests were built and eggs laid, some brave kid would climb the tree crawl out onto branches, and steal several eggs. The idea being, to leave a few eggs for the mother bird to hatch. Although, some kids claimed that once a nest had been robbed, the hen would never return, leaving the remaining eggs to rot or be eaten by squirrels. I never knew whether that was true or just used as an excuse to go back later and steal the remaining eggs. Of course, every so often, someone fell, or a branch broke along with a kid's limbs.

Snaring the eggs was only the first part of the egg collecting mission. The next task was getting down from the tree with the eggs in your pocket or mouth without cracking them and having them spill out over you or inside your mouth. Then finally, scratching a small hole in both ends of the egg so that you could blow out the yoke and white, without breaking the shell was another.

The number of eggs in your collection was a treasure to brag about. It was one more collectible item that a boy guarded at all costs like stamps, bottle caps, marbles, sports cards, and train numbers. Collections that gave you status.

Then there were dens and tree houses to build. This meant bits of wood, cardboard boxes, wire, string, and rope had to be found, and your father's hammer and nails spirited away into wooded areas.

For some reason, girls were not allowed to participate in most of our games and pastimes except for building a treehouse. In fact, girls and especially sisters were usually frozen out of boys' activities. They had the habit of snitching to your mother or telling you what not to do. They didn't go scrumping for apples from the farmer's orchards, smoke cigarettes, or raid someone else's den.

And what about now, I wonder. Working mothers and kids bottled up in apartments playing games on computers or Xbox, gawking at iPhones, controlled and restricted for safety. What about those kids? Will they ever run free?

Will gaps between my generation and theirs widen even further as they look at grandparents and we look at them and wonder what to say? I wonder what they think as grandma has to be shown more than once how to use a computer, while at the same time they don't know how to build a campfire, roast chestnuts, tie granny knots, or trade birds eggs for marbles.

Oh, oh, there's Angus, the scruffy dog from across the road. I hope he doesn't crap on my lawn again. Every so often, he does that. I don't know why, and yet Jack, the black retriever next door, never does. Jack visits me several times a week and stands at the back door until I let him in. He then finds a rug that he likes, hangs out for an hour or two, and then returns home.

I complained to my neighbor about his dog's toiletry habits, but he didn't seem overly concerned. So now I shovel Angus's shit up and deposit it on his lawn.

Filling the Gaps

I notice that when you have time on your hands, the mind starts to break free from life's daily schedule. *What day is it?* being the common question. Your mind allows itself to open up and step outside the daily, weekly routine that you have fashioned for yourself as you interact less and less with people.

In isolation and with the restricted movement of people, you may be surprised by those quiet moments. Those spaces between generated noise. And slowly, almost imperceptibly, your brain fills the space. You find yourself slowing down, reconsidering, internalizing.

We are told the brain never shuts down, so what is mine doing? Is it taking the time to reappraise, resist the past or the foreseeable future? Will the unconsidered creep in? Watch this space. That's all I can say.

In America, we have a TV channel called PBS (Public Broadcasting Service), which is the only station partly funded by the government. All other national broadcasting channels are funded by advertising. I never watch any of those channels live and only record a few of their feature shows. The amount of advertising far outweighs most of the content of those channels. And many of their daily shows are low-level entertainment. Why? I don't know.

But I often wonder, is it in response to demand, a reaction to the general audience's perceived acuity, or is it the purposeful dumbing down of the general population? There are several reasons why I consider the latter, and one of them is because the Republican Party or "Far Right" is very opposed to PBS. They don't feel obliged to ensure that the general public has the right to unbiased programming, especially from an independent media outlet that could be considered intellectual, educational, progressive, or noteworthy. I won't go into the merits of the political strategy here, except to say the GOP claim that the government should not be involved in a media entertainment business. But of course, that is not the real reason.

Dumb down the message, feed them shit as Steve Bannon would say, harness the mob, secure the rich with tax cuts, access their money. Split the nation. Those are the real reasons. Is it really as evident and simple as that? I'm thinking, *yes*.

Mind you, PBS news is becoming a bit tiresome. I think they are overreaching with the "let us be politically correct" look. The two token white guys take a back seat while the five or six women of varying types across society's spectrum, two of whom are almost inarticulate, try to convince us they know what they are talking about.

There again, does all this really matter—we're here, we're gone, and very soon no one will know that we existed. We look for a point; there is no point, only procreation, a bacon sandwich, and a warm bed, if you're lucky. Maybe the American system is right after all; take what you can when you can.

I must admit, I'm feeling a bit down in the dumps today. Perhaps I should open that box of chocolates Doreen bought me.

Cave Painting

I was talking on the telephone to a friend of mine who is a painter, of pictures, not houses. Painters are interesting because they usually have a different slant on life. I would like to be a painter, but unfortunately, I do not have the skill set or the eye.

But I can sometimes imagine myself walking through a field or down towards the sea with an easel and brushes, a cigarette dangling from my mouth, oblivious, wearing a straw hat, raggedy shirt, shorts, and sandals. Clothes that are timeless, for artists that is. Then losing myself in the image, the color, and creation, knowing that I can make the field blue and sky yellow if the urge takes me, a pig pink with wings, or Doreen's mother in her underwear. It would be entirely up to me.

Of course, before the camera, it was only the artists who were engaged in capturing reality. Or was it reality? According to the Christian church, it was: *Ya wanna see a miracle, Jesus, resurrection, heaven—step this way*. Then all of that kinda changed when Kodak arrived. Now it has changed even more because of the computer. Now almost anyone can doctor photographs to make the world and those in it anything they want. You can make Skinny Minny look like Dolly Parton if you want to.

So, where's the artist amongst all of these changes? Many of them are in the emotional room, creating paintings and sculptures that, for the life of me, I cannot understand. Although I have to admit some of them are eye-catching, even breathtaking. However, I always have that nagging question running around in my head as I try to figure them out. Okay, but can these guys who dribble paint on bits of canvas or draw body parts in all the wrong places, and

29

such like, *can they really paint?* You know, like Rembrandt or Turner and all the others?

By the way, that reminds me of the movie, *The Mill and the Cross*. An excellent film about Bruegel the Elder painting one of his medieval village scenes. The film brings the village, and its occupants to life as the painting on canvas is being filled in. What is particularly striking is the silence throughout the movie. And that is how it must have been in a village in those days. Silent.

In those days, ordinary people must have taken to their bed not long after nightfall and woke at the crack of dawn to the occasional sound of birds, a cow, and someone talking, or a creaking wagon making its way down a lane. There wouldn't be unrelenting noise from motor vehicles, machinery, airplanes, or the slamming of doors, etc. And that thought brought to my mind the first few months during this pandemic when most people isolated themselves, and partial silence descended upon us.

It was then that I realized how we usually live with constant noise impinging on us at varying levels. Funnily enough, it is also now that I notice more wild animals openly appearing and reclaiming spaces within my neighborhood. A fox, calm as you like, walking in the center of our road outside this house during the middle of the day; families of rabbits and squirrels taking over the lawns; coyotes and hawks hanging around; along with a family of skunk who took it upon themselves to live under my shed.

More recently, I am wondering about the motives and demands for art. And that takes me all the way back to the beginning. What prompted the early Homo sapiens to paint animal scenes and make imprints? What was this desire to leave a permanent image of what we do, who we are?

A desire to record that we were here has continued throughout the ages, and as far as I am aware, no other animal does that. So I think it must have something to do with the brain's development that encourages people to tell stories, record information, pass it on, and search for meaning. Perhaps that is the secret strength of our species, the reason why we have been so successful.

Archeologists say that our human ancestors' control of fire took place over a million years ago. I think that this must have been the giant leap forward because at that point, not only could you keep warm, store food, and cook food, but you could see in the dark. And this allowed our species to while away their time by drawing pictures and extending communication.

The earliest cave art, which is over 40,000 years old, was found in Indonesia. The most famous or prehistoric elaborate paintings to be found so far are in a Spanish cave. They are ochre and charcoal images of handprints, bison, and horses and are thought to be around 36,000 years old. I guess when you don't have a radio, TV, knitting needles, or a book to read, that's what you do—paint on the wall.

And now here we all are, thinking this isolation is terrible. Imagine what it must have been like in those days. And just consider that the human painting activity was developing throughout the world during the same period by people who had never met each other, and who lived 8,000 miles apart. No copyright laws were needed then.

Like so many other happenstances such as the development of language, writing, and the building of pyramids, wall painting is another example of the human brain evolving and responding in the same manner, at about the same time, across the world. Give or take a thousand years or so. Which, by the way, is no time at all in evolutionary terms.

When considering these similar evolving or trending occurrences, and even though it is hard to accept, this tells me that people in darkest Africa, inner Mongolia, and similar less advanced places, without contact to the modern world, should eventually learn to fly to the moon, develop the computer, and discover DNA. *Should,* that is, but so far, based upon their output over thousands of years, it seems they are unlikely to do so.

Wow! What a conclusion. I'm not sure whether I can fully go along with the logic, but there it is; excluding the hand of God, evolution through necessity and curiosity was only a matter of time for some, but not for others who hardly developed at all. I'm going to have to explain all of this to Doreen. She'll tell me I'm going bonkers.

Retired

Looking out of the window at a few squirrels and two birds on the lawn, I'm wondering if they are the same squirrels and birds I saw yesterday, last week, last month. I can't tell. They say crows can recognize the human face. I have to wonder about that. Anyway, I'm thinking about retirement and what that has meant for myself and most people. For some unknown reason, the thought came to me just like that. Or perhaps it is the currently enforced inertia that brought retirement to mind.

I clearly remember once being in a conference room at the office, and upon looking around, my mind paused for a moment because I suddenly realized that I was the oldest person in the room. To my amazement, time had flashed by. What happened? It didn't seem so long ago when I was the youngest one in the room. I wanted to shout, *What the hell happened?*

Those squirrels and birds out there know nothing about retirement. Jack, who's paying one of his social calls, has decided to lie on the floor beside me. He also knows nothing about retirement. Actually, he knows nothing about work. All we get out of him is an occasional bark at the mailman or a twig. And for that, his food is handed to him along with free board and lodge. He was born into retirement. In fact, he probably thinks we work for him. I suppose he's right.

I think the word *retire* is a bit of an all-inclusive term. Retire to bed, retire from a career, retire a cricket team, and retire to a French villa—chance would be a fine thing.

I remember a couple of years before we went into lockdown standing behind a sad-looking chap in Stop & Shop's check-out line. He stood to one side and said to me, "You go ahead, I'm retired."

I think I was older than him. But it didn't bother me; I took him up on his offer. Perhaps he was short-sighted. Why sad-looking, I wondered.

Except for those retiring to a villa in Corfu, perhaps for most people, retirement connotes unhappiness caused by a sense of resignation, a sense of nothing better to do. I guess for many, it's somewhat like becoming isolated. That is like we are now. Slowly, bit by bit, people, things, interests, and energy just fall away.

Maybe it's time to come up with a new word for this activity—a word symbolizing the freedom being granted by society. I mean, I ask myself, how many times in my daily grind over a fifty-year period have I had to endure pointless meetings, deal with the pressures of the job, the politics, the tedium, the impositions, disappointments, and untethered ambition of a younger obnoxious know-it-all git.

Mind you, in my case, I have to admit my work held a lot more interest than digging holes or laying bricks. But then there comes a time when you enter the office one morning and hear that there will be staff cuts, and your stomach tightens because you may be the one to have your job function eliminated, encouraged to retire voluntarily, or fired. In other words, you're no longer wanted. The final bell. *Hello, we've decided to set you free.*

"See how lucky you are, Jack? Here, have another biscuit."

Of course, that never happened to me; I knew when it was time to go. I had another life to get on with, and all the time in the world left for me to find out what that would be.

"Know what I mean, Jack? Of course, you do."

"Is that you talking to that dog again. He'll be talking back at you one of these days," Doreen said, as she came into the room and plopped a cup of tea on the desk, and left with a smirk on her face.

It is surprising how few men are prepared for this eventuality. I say *men* because I'm assuming that most women handle retirement more easily, but there again, these days, perhaps I'm wrong. Like the guy in line at Stop & Shop, he had all the time in the world because he'd lost his identity. In other words, *We are what we do?*

Moreover, it is quite noticeable how people often identify themselves by what they do. "Hi, I'm Dave. I was a lawyer," or "I'm the firefighter who lives across the road. Here's my number," or "I'm Jeffrey, a proctologist, we could keep in touch if you like."

So, as long as you have a good health care plan (and believe me, if you haven't, you are screwed), then this retirement gig is okay. "Hi, I'm Cliff. I do what my wife tells me to do, have a garden, a computer on which to write, and a universe of like-minded creative people, and no, I don't care how screwed up your old company is or how many pianos you tuned, or whatever you do each day."

Before Covid, there was little about my retirement that was retiring. I kept busy, had fun, hopped on my bike now and then, and visited Dan up the road. We'd sit around his fire; he'd drink vodka and put the world to right, I'd have a coke. I'd visit the library, plant things in my garden, and paint something. Now, of course, I Zoom and marvel at how everyone on the screen seems so young and sane compared to me. Oh, I nearly forgot I also have a daily game of Bananagrams with Doreen.

"And Jack, I'll let you in on a secret: one of these days before we all get out of lockdown or disappear, I'm going to start beating her at that game."

The Debate

Am I seeing the end? Which will come first, the end of Trump's reign or the Covid vaccine? As much as I want my isolation to end, I would prefer Trump's landslide mutilation to happen first.

Was it my imagination the other night as I watched from my sanctuary two old geezers sort of debate each other. Let's be fair; it wasn't very inspiring, revealing, or cultivated.

Both geezers under the lights. One like a dumb, over-the-hill game show host, stiffly leaning forward due to his shoe lifts and tight corset, which made his fat bum stick out. The other guy, gripping both sides of his podium most of the time; like an old man trying to avoid wandering off somewhere in vague bewilderment, looking for the toilet.

Both gladiators had been trained and tuned-up since last we had seen them—If he says this, you say that and duck, but try not to box yourself in a corner. Suppose he throws a left, weave, and counter. Keep substance brief; we don't want to show people how dumb you are with a yellow wig and orange make-up. Are you sure you're not gay? Just a thought.

And you—we don't want you to stumble over words, so keep to the four- and definitely no more than five-letter kinda words, go with something like, *Give me a break*, that's a good one, and for Christ's sake, don't stare up at the ceiling when trying to conjure up a thought. By the way, if either one of you guys are dying for a pee, think of Hilary Clinton and tighten your buttocks. Also, whatever you do, don't fart until the mike is muted.

There they were, leaders of the world: con man and criminal or criminal and con man, take your pick, and we flexed our minds waiting for the throwing of handbags and name-calling.

There they were doddering about like supreme court judges in starched robes wondering what ordinary people do with their genitals while they cook up some nebulous opinions and look forward to their mashed potatoes, peas, and soup, and a glass of warm milk.

And all the while, I am watching Trump's eyes. Can I see weakness, a hint of desperation? Is he, a supposedly veteran negotiator, feeling things slip away, his pitch falling flat as the repartee loses fire? Is the glaze and pursed lips and shit-faced smile telling me he knows he's running out of phlegm? Is he beginning to fear loss and what that will mean as Obama's man—that nasty "old Joe" facing off with him, a 50-year veteran of running this game—is pushing him down the gangplank as he talks about liars and thugs and crazy connivers? Is Joe going to let him escape alive or push him off the end of the plank and feed him to the sharks that are waiting to clean up? Jail sounds good.

How do I get out of this one? he's thinking as his private parts shrink. And all those behind him, like Eric, Ivanka, and the rest are beginning to realize their world is about to come apart. Is Moscow that bad?

Was that the hysterical look I was seeing, or was it my fanciful imagination as the other guy with dead-pan eyes theatrically pointed at the camera and was able to address us with such electrifying clarity. Bone-chilling statements such as, "Look, here's the deal" or "Number one" and then proved he could count to number two. What should we have expected? Could we have asked for more?

Sure!!

Me, I would have liked a short interval with Mitch McConnell doing a foxtrot gliding across the stage with

Nancy Pelosi or Elizabeth Warren drop-kicking Ted Cruz in the crotch. In the meantime, Biden's son could show us a video of himself spaced out in a bathtub smoking a joint.

That's the sort of thing I was thinking as lights dimmed and the curtain closed on the men who rule the world, and I say to my Doreen, "Don't worry, it's all part of the democratic process; this is why we pay taxes—for entertainment—not like those miserable socialist sods in dung heaps like Zurich or Clacton-on-Sea."

I asked my pal up the road, "Was the same thing going through your head at the time, was it? Or were you watching repeats of *Doc Martin*?"

Deep in the Weeds

I was watching a nature thing the other day while at the same time continuing to think about isolation. By the way, it's interesting how the English language drops the 'e' whenever modifying the particular verb to end with 'ing,' except in Britain for the word *ageing*. What is an ing word, you may ask? A present participle, or gerund. One can never be sure. My friends Diane and Mary will know something about that.

I was also thinking about my pal John's poem, talking about the young being pushed out of the nest, moving on, and striking new paths of their own in order to make it in this world and only occasionally returning home for; Christmas, a wedding, or funeral perhaps. I then realized that in nature, animals rarely do this.

Many of them stay together in family packs, united, knowing that they are safer and stronger together. Of course, some species do wander off on their own, but perhaps they are the less successful ones. Success, even individual success, comes from being within and brought up by an established society. However, traveling and mixing with others undoubtedly improves the advancement of knowledge through the exchange of ideas and experience.

So what made the human species develop its extraordinary brainpower well beyond all other species? My mother used to say sprouts were good for the brain and carrots for the eyes—or was it the other way around? Anyway, this superior brainpower initially allowed one of the weakest species on Earth to become totally dominant. All due to carrots or sprouts, apparently. And then it, the superior mentality, enabled its members to fight each other. The strong defeating the weak in order to further natural progression and bolster Darwin's evolution theory. All the while developing societies through which individuals were allowed to express new ideas, further triggering the brain and learning process. This has especially been the case since religion took a back seat.

Now, after careening along at ever-increasing speed (now hyper-supersonic, I'm told) pushing humanity to either further triumphs or extinction, we've come up against the ever-present virus. That is the other living organism that has always been here, fighting to rule the world. Is it possible that being forced into isolation for too long will slow us down, dumb down our neurons, and leave us more exposed?

As interaction and exchanges at this time become more difficult for our species, the rest of nature stands by and looks on while we fight the new virus, knowing that all we can do is push back, but not totally eradicate it. Will the virus mutate faster than a vaccine can be redeveloped, will the government and society's institutions be weakened? Is this the start of a long fight that our species may not win?

There's a black-and-white movie here somewhere— mad scientists, each sporting one glass eye, a hunched back, and gammy leg. They're moving glass test tubes, crucibles, and Bunsen burners around while cackling and humming out of tune. In the meantime, Eric (I think it was him) shoots an elephant—my friend Wayne will know the scene.

On the other hand, if you listen to the guy with a melon head and Harvard law degree, Pompeo, it could all be a Chinese plot. They, the "yellow peril," are going to suddenly turn up in New York harbor with butcher's knives and forks yelling, "Corona, corona, we come from Wuhan, and take over country."

Seriously, this could be it. The whole shebang could go up in smoke as the mentally disabled orange guy with plastic teeth lights the blue paper to set off our 20,000 nuclear bombs, or Melania—or is it Ivana, or Ivanka, I can't keep up—goes back to pole dancing. After all, whoever would have thought that we would have a Humpty Dumpty sitting in the Whitehouse as we wait around mesmerized in isolation. Now we have no one to fight but ourselves.

Just some thoughts I'm spouting. You don't have to go along with them, but one has to admit when you stand way back from this situation, these are biblical times, and that is one crazy book.

An Autumn Day

It's mid-morning. A cold wind from the northwest cut through the air, making my eyes water as I walked my daughter's dog around the block. She usually comes to visit us for an hour three times a week, and we stay six feet apart with our masks on. I called my neighbor and asked them to make sure Jack stayed home.

My daughter's dog is named Nelly; I never asked why. It's part pit bull and very territorial.

On our walks, Nelly has the annoying habit of being unable to decide where she wants to poop. She'll select a spot waddle back and forth, sniffing here and there, and I think, *Great, she's finally going to go*, only to once again watch her change her mind and head off to another spot. She does this again and again. It can be annoying on a nice day, but when it's cold, like today—infuriating. But I shouldn't complain because she is forcing me to stay fit, which I notice is something I'm prone not to do as I loaf about the house succumbing to lethargy, putting things off until the next day, like an incarcerated jailbird.

I'm not sure when it was that my eyes started to water in the cold. Tears running down my cheeks. Anyone would think I was crying. I guess it's one of those age-related things; eyes watering, time accelerating, the distance to my feet getting further and further away as I attempt to put on socks. These days, I sit on the second to last step of my stairs, putting my foot on the first to reach my toes to pull on my socks or tie my sneakers.

At the beginning of the year, I got my eyes checked and found I needed reading glasses. This didn't surprise me. I remembered that way back when I was in school, we studied the eye. I learned that as you age, the muscles around the lens change, which alters the focus to nearsightedness. That is, from being able to see objects that are far away to be able to see close-up objects, something like that. There's a technical term for this. But what was surprising is that the change of vision thing did not affect me until I was over 70 years old.

CVS glasses do the trick, but I have to remember to take them off before moving about; otherwise, I get dizzy. Oh yes, and there's that thing about remembering where I put them. Doreen reckons she is going to tape them to my ears. It is one of those annoyances that goes along with getting old, although I have to say the alternative kinda sucks.

I'm supposed to have my eyes checked next week, but I don't know. Why take the risk of catching Covid just to learn whether my eyesight has gotten worse? I can figure that out for myself. Right? My mind's made up, I'll cancel.

"Don't forget the garden," Doreen had said.

"Yes, you're right; it's time to dig up the dahlias. I'll put the tubers in a cardboard box with compost and store them in the basement," I said.

"And don't forget those ferns need to be in the atrium." Doreen was in her supervisory mode. I always try to resist this because bringing plants into the house involves moving couches, washing off pots, and checking them for bugs. One year, we didn't check and had roly-poly bugs crawling all over the place. We've had the ferns for about twenty years, periodically repotting them into larger pots. Each time I bring them in, they're bigger and heavier. But Doreen likes them, and there is no arguing with Doreen once she sets her mind on something.

"Let's just move the Norfolk Pine to the other side of the atrium next to the TV. The small bureau will have to go into the living room. We'll use the iron tables from the deck." And so it continued.

As I moved one item, she would decide to move others until most of the furniture, pictures, and carpets found a new residence. The next day I woke up in pain. I'd put my back out.

"What are you doing?" Doreen asked.

"I've pulled something in my back; it's from moving all of that damn furniture," I said.

"Yes, but what are you doing?" she asked again.

"It's an exercise that will help the healing process."

"You need a heating pad," she said.

"I know that. I'll use it afterward," I said with some irritation.

"No need to be snippy. I had nothing to do with it. It is no use blaming me. You ought to be more careful at your age," was her reply.

"I, oh, never mind," I said and heard the tick-tock of the clock. It was going to be a long day.

Out of Sight, Out of Mind

I was reading something which I found quite interesting. I can't remember who wrote most of what follows—not me. But anyway, I'm going with it because it would have been something I'd say. Not the spectrum part, but most of the rest. Especially as I sit wondering if all of this is sane. Is it the future?

From here on in, is it true that we are going to have multiple vaccines every year or three months, to make sure our kids and friends don't kill us? Or if a waiter sneezes, will it be off I go to la-la land and talk to my wife from the grave?

The thing is, there is a thought that if you are human, you can expect to see and know everything. I mean, upon opening our eyes, we think we see the whole world out there. However, what has been made abundantly clear by those who say they know—that is, the sort of people who study things and don't hang out with Trumpsters—they say that when you look at the electromagnetic spectrum, you see one-tenth of one-billionth of the information residing out there.

What we see is, in fact, called visible light, and everything else passing through our bodies is entirely invisible to us. Crikey!

Therefore, even though we accept the reality presented to us, the fact is, we are only seeing what's really going on through a small window.

Having been enlightened by this, I'm thinking, *Now we're getting somewhere. I need to find out more.*

But then I ask myself, *Why don't we see everything?* And I get an answer from a guy who seems to spend a lot of his time looking through thick pebble-like glasses into a microscope before doing something on a computer.

"Sight as we know it is irrelevant," he says with a slight smirk. "Think energy, the quantum field, and resonance." He goes on to say, "We are multidimensional and are stuck in the 3D world of consciousness."

Then I think, this is like talking to a priest. You've probably noticed that a priest always has an answer which seems okay, but is just beyond complete comprehension.

Later on, I read, "The changing world order is upon us. Soon electric energy will be transmitted without wires over thousands of miles." Mind you, I don't know about that, but if some guy from the West Coast is saying it will be so, then it could be true. They think differently out there.

Proceeding on, I learn that someone else is spouting out that creative destruction and the precious fragility of life is an illusion of time, that space is the intimacy of human experience and incomprehension of the universe. Geez!

By now, my mind is entirely up the pole, and I'm saying to myself this could mean anything. Does my clever grandson know this? More to the point, I have no way of knowing whether Jesus walked on water.

I go on to wonder, is this what internalizing means? Do others think I know what I think, and think they know what I think, and think I know what they believe? Do I assume it is a coincidence that someone thought what I was thinking or that something happened more or less the way I hoped? Does one suddenly remember a person from way back and then find out that something of significance just happened to them? Is it more than predictable when general opinion about turns?

As I move closer towards death, why do I feel my parents' presence almost continuously, yet I didn't ponder over them very much decades ago. Are my eyes moving further back into my head, and did the wall just say something?

As artificial intelligence advances and computers inside robots have conversations with one another, will the transformations of their knowledge be passed on to others? Will they experience the same mental growth as the brain of the human? Are we trapped by what we do see, totally oblivious of what we don't see? Who can conceive of more than three dimensions? Who lives in the fourth and fifth dimension?

My other grandson, who's also very smart by the way, once told me there are ten dimensions. I said, "Oh, really, I was thinking the same thing." While, at the same time, wondering what the hell he was talking about. How much don't we know is basically the big question.

Energy cannot be destroyed, only changed. Wait, does that apply to us? I suppose so. There again, where does religion fit in? According to what some people think, religion is an artificial construct conveniently coming to terms with the unknown and unkind while providing comfort, fear, and distress. In our isolation, do we currently feel this to be so?

Do viruses have a form of religion guiding them on their way as they fight for survival? Do they have feelings of desire? Do they, in the biblical and textural sense, know we exist? Do they admire and fear us? Do they see what we see? Is it an endless war between us?

If you can, without question, follow a guy dressed in a white frock, who pontificates and lives in a large gold-adorned palace in Rome, then consider this: Why not an orange-faced bloke who lives in a fake gold hotel in Florida, who constantly lies and cheats even at golf?

People are fickle. One minute they're alive, next minute they're dead, and no one hardly notices.

Theodicy—The Moralist Must Always Be Outraged

I'm not sure if you are listening, but I'm suggesting we are in the confines of what "is," what exists at the moment of perception, the only rationale being what we conceive as right and wrong. The dark and light of things, the unknown as we strive to understand and make sense of it all.

We are undisputed, sitting at the top of the food chain, preying on every other thing on Earth—animal, vegetable, and mineral—for our survival and pleasure. And we are ignorant of universal knowledge. Thus the uninformed with unsatisfied curiosity, while experiencing the cycles of life and death, are unwilling to accept that we are insignificant and simply belong to the "is."

One way we deal with this situation is by creating religions that try to explain the mystery of life and salve our conscience as we go on our merry way, while at the same time crusade against those who choose to think otherwise.

When looking around, we notice that other species have not made this leap through evolving development. Also, as we observe what's taking place with Homo sapiens, we notice that the American native, aboriginal people in darkest Africa, and others, of their own cognizance, have not been able to make the scientific journey from the lever to the screw thread, from the arrow to the airplane, from language to algebra.

And the list goes on and on as gaps between people over centuries get wider and wider. Why, after the Persians and Romans left, could some pick up the pieces and carry on towards enlightenment and others could not? Some believe in the Holy Spirit, some in Shiva, and who knows what else.

And so we come to my pal Wayne's thought that there must be a power of an ambiguous nature because of the existence of evil. But the question is, why did a merciful God allow evil, and for that matter as far as I'm concerned, why did God allow Trump to become President, a Donald cult, and pandemic to exist simultaneously?

Then I say to myself, not to worry; It's a test, and this too shall pass. Soon all that we will be left with are bodies to bury, and who the hell was he, Trump that is, and what'll we do with the MAGA caps and t-shirts? On the other hand, some may ask, how will we carry on without him? A man, who, they may say, was misunderstood by many. A man who was more popular than Jesus in his heyday.

Of course, God and his spokespeople are not very visible when thousands die for no apparent reason, and fascism takes over in America egged on by the evangelicals. Do they secretly crave for the gas ovens?

When considering all that has gone before, it seems to me that in order to satisfy the Trump cult, the only solution is for Donald to make the ultimate sacrifice. It's the only way.

After all, we have the obligatory biblical plague, but now shrines have to be built, stories told, miracles performed, and leather-bound books written containing his tweets and words of wisdom, including those slurred pearls of insight that are so deeper-than-deep such that their meaning escapes comprehension.

They must all be studied, along with his feces, and we must continue to stamp his name on high, hold memorial rallies so that he's never forgotten. So that his disciples can tend his flock and glorify his name, drink his blood, sell his bits of bone and teeth, and occasionally put the thumbscrews to non-believers.

What are we, as we move beyond crucifixion and resurrection, towards one more deity? Is he the future? Or will we take a deep breath, calm down, write it off as a bad experience, give the kids back to their mothers, kiss Madam Merkel on both cheeks and say no to coal, tell Macron that he's not really a pansy, tell Putin to sod off and the Chinese that they can keep their 1.4 billion population, clean up central America, remove all tax holidays, loopholes, and incentives or whatever else, and go cold turkey? That is, respond to the wake-up call, build from the bottom, because rest assured the rich will always be among us and evil walks the land.

Yes, you may have guessed it. There were fireworks, car horns, bells ringing, and people singing in the streets, and I am so happy we have dumped Trump. In the meantime, I have learned a lot about Hitler, Eric, Cruz, the electoral college, the Constitution, weakness of democracy, strength of democracy, perils of globalization, vengeance of the deprived, and Doreen.

So, for the moment, we stepped back from the precipice, and I thank goodness, have put off returning to the Land of Our Fathers. Because over there, it is always raining, and I am too old for all that crap. Here in America, we have turned a corner; the leaves have fallen, winter is here, it is time for reflection and then renewal. We do not need re-education camps, just, fairness and respect for one another.

I am not sure why I am saying all of this. It must be my relief upon realizing that democracy and sanity almost works. Now, what can be done to win over those 70 odd million people who voted for Trump and the rancorous Republican Party, I wonder?

Outside My Window

Some say the universe is vast—at least 100 billion light-years across. According to them, possibly any size, up to infinite and is perfectly arrayed for creating stars, galaxies, and other complex systems.

I read a short article, and it had to be short if it was about all that space stuff, since it is difficult to relate to. The article stated that astronomers had discovered the most enormous explosion in the universe since the Big Bang—a blast that blew a hole the size of 15 Milky Ways in the surrounding space. Supposedly this happened a few hundred million years ago, hundreds of light-years away from Earth.

By the way, there may be between 100 and 400 billion stars in the Milky Way, which happens to be just one of 140 billion or so galaxies. How do you digest something like that? Not only that, but how do you actually measure and count this stuff with any kind of accuracy.

Closer to home, I wonder how many people know that it would take seven hours to reach Pluto from here at the speed of light. That may not sound much, but if you consider light travels at 186,000 miles per second, that's when you say, "Wow!"

Another illuminating thought that comes to mind is that the nearest star known as Proxima Centauri is 4.3 light-years away which happens to be a small skip in galactic terms, but for us to reach it by spaceship would take approximately 80 thousand years. So, for those who still believe in UFOs, stick that in your pipe and smoke it.

Furthermore, given all of that, we may be only one of a million advanced civilizations. But the catch is the distance between any two could be 200 light-years. So we can see that within the universe, worlds are precious. Carl Sagan wrote that if we are randomly inserted into the universe, the chances you would be on or near a planet with any life form would be less than one in a billion trillion.

These kinds of universe numbers make my head spin; however, it is claimed that only six digits, in particular, govern our universe, and if they were to change ever so slightly, things would not be as they are now. For example, hydrogen has to be converted to helium in a precise manner. Lower the value by 0.007%, and no transformation would take place, and the universe would consist of hydrogen and nothing else. Raise the value slightly, and hydrogen would have long been exhausted.

No one knows how long an atom will survive. When we die, our atoms will disassemble and, I imagine over time, move off to find new uses elsewhere, as part of a leaf or human or drop of dew.

Half a million atoms shoulder-to-shoulder could hide behind a human hair, and yet an atom made up of protons and electrons and neutrons is almost all space. The neutrons and protons combine and make up the nucleus which is one-millionth of a billionth of the entire volume of its atom. I'm sure you'll agree all of this is beyond comprehension really. But not only that, it is reckoned in the school science classroom that the human being is mainly made up of water. Well, I say it is mainly made up of space.

Of course, as you delve into the world of astronomy and guesstimating the reason for something happening or not— black holes, big bangs, parallel universes, multi dimensions and all the rest of it—you become even more confused and quickly conclude that you are so small as to be insignificant.

I think it was again Carl Sagan who said, "Observation: I can't see a thing. Conclusion: Dinosaurs." I like that; it says a lot.

Among other things he wrote was, "We inhabit a universe where atoms are made in the centers of stars; where each second, a thousand suns are born; where life is sparked by sunlight and lightning in the airs and waters of youthful planets; where the explosion sometimes makes the raw material for biological evolution of a star halfway across the Milky Way; where a thing as beautiful as a galaxy is formed a hundred billion times—a cosmos of quasars and quarks, snowflakes and fireflies, where there may be black holes and other universes and extraterrestrial civilizations whose radio messages are at this moment reaching the Earth. How pallid by comparison are the pretensions of superstition and pseudoscience; how important it is for us to pursue and understand the science that characteristically describes human endeavor."

Now that's a lot to take in, and it seems to me that those thoughts beg the question: *Do I believe there must be a purpose, a reason for us, perhaps a higher purpose?* Of course, we will never know, but one has to wonder what the heck is going on. The idea of a man's contrived religion, conjured up by flat-earthers, being true is a stretch. And how various groups have played it out over the years leaves something not to be desired.

Not only that, but as we hide from this pandemic, you have to wonder why we spend so much effort and money on space exploration and all that imaginative schoolboy stuff. Especially when so many things have to be put right here on Earth, not least of which is saving humanity from itself. The only logical explanation for space spending is, as I have said before, military dominance here on Earth, plain and simple.

On that sour note, Doreen and I will mask up, put our gloves and glasses on, and go to the store.

Above and Beyond

Talking about out there and beyond once again got me to thinking about space. The first reported sighting of a man levitating, which was considered legitimate at the time, was that of Saint Joseph of Cupertino. For those who have their doubts, some say there was no reason for the church to have fabricated these reports because he was considered a distraction.

In fact, he received many cease and desist warnings from the church mainly because he could gather large crowds. Larger than they could.

This caused him to be placed under house arrest. Interestingly enough, at the same time as Galileo. One was a mystic, the other a force for science, yet both faced the same inquisitors. Saint Joseph claimed that he could float because he was in a state of altered consciousness. Why not? I suppose he had to say something.

Even today, the mystical stuff somehow survives within the heat of science, and there have been vague reports of yogis being able to levitate due to the power of the mind. But most people go along with science, believing there is no such thing as the power of mental energy and that it cannot create a physical force capable of acting against the pull of gravity.

So what does that mean? No matter how hard I concentrate my mind-power, my feet will remain firmly on the ground, and my pen is not going to move across the desk. Now, I have to admit that is disappointing.

But wait a minute, what about that guy Haim Eshed, a highly respected and qualified former head of Israel's military defense space directorate? He claims there are extraterrestrials in contact with America and an underground base in the depths of Mars.

Perhaps not surprisingly this so-called revelation happened on Trump's watch. At about the same time, Trump told the world that America now had a new military branch called Space Force, and its focus is on space as a military domain for the U.S. That is, for protecting satellites and communications and focusing on geopolitics in new terrain. Whatever that means, and you can be sure that whatever it means, is not good.

For example, "Be aware—or is it *beware*—I'm doing this for your own protection." If a statement like that doesn't sound off alarm bells in other countries, I'll eat my hat. By the way, I think this, let's say, unusual revelation happened just after Trump made Netanyahu and most Jews his lifelong friends by moving the American embassy to Jerusalem.

Of course, I'm sitting here thinking, what next? First saints flying, gurus levitating, and now an 87-year-old guy with impeccable qualifications who happens to have just written a book is spouting off about us being able to speak an alien language. Meanwhile, we are being attacked by an alien virus, and the culprits for causing this pandemic—that is, the Chinese—are holding up their hands, saying, "Don't look at us, we know nothing about it," as they keep their crematorium furnaces running 24 hours a day.

Maybe Trump is an alien. After all, as I mentioned previously, he talked about swallowing a light bulb and drinking Clorox or something like that. Now you have to admit, that's pretty weird.

Naturally, or perhaps not, looney birds believe in all of this stuff: mysticism, pseudoscience, flat earth, UFOs, aliens, miracles, swallowing electricity, and extremist religions. And there will be more of them like me, who'll be prepared to say whatever, as long as it gets us out of this mess.

It is quite interesting to consider that on most days, many of us don't believe in all of this off-the-wall-sounding fiction, including angels and fairies, and yet, scientists tell us things exist we cannot see or feel. Such as electrons, protons, and quarks, which have been discovered by experimental deduction.

For some reason, maybe because the science guys wear white coats, we go along with what they tell us. Mind you, if Sid, my barber, who wears a white jacket, says he's willing to tell me my future just by looking at my dog's entrails, I don't know.

What About the Future

All of this thinking time due to the pandemic brings nostalgic memories. We fondly remember the past and forget those tough times when advancing from horse and carts to the Internet, from the fear of tuberculosis to stem cells and organ replacements, from day trips to Barry Island to flying around the world. Are we better off? Undoubtedly so.

That is, I and the likes of me are. But what about future generations? That's what I wonder. Are we making a better life for them, and will they be able to clean up the mess we are leaving behind?

Besides climate issues and wealth gaps that have yet to be dealt with, I have two other areas of concern. The first is eugenics associated with genetics.

Why? Because now that we have been able to determine the human genome sequence, we have entered an area of gene editing. In fact, I recently read that a Chinese scientist performed a groundbreaking experiment by producing twins who had been edited as embryos. This was a game-changer, and for this remarkable but unauthorized achievement, the scientist was sent to prison for three years. Or at least that's what the Chinese tell us.

However, I am not so sure whether putting him in prison will change anything going forward, because once a breakthrough in scientific research takes place, there's no turning back the clock. Some fear that this breakthrough will enable humans to play God. Scientists will not only be removing a gene responsible for an inherited disease, but may also be able to enhance children into so-called designer babies.

Come to think of it, I vaguely remember Japanese scientists claimed they produced mature mouse eggs and sperm from stem cells and used them to breed healthy mouse pups. Their published paper said the next step would be to try to make mature human eggs and produce human sperm. Now you have to admit this is a dark corner that we may all be entering. I was impressed by that movie *Blade Runner*, but not anxious to believe that the real world could end up that way.

Whether the idea is repulsive or not, in my opinion, eugenics seems the likely outcome, and it could turn Darwin's theory "survival of the fittest" on its head. In fact, perhaps not surprisingly, the Chinese are busily using Artificial Intelligence to build lifelike robots. Mind you, why they want to do that when their current population stands at well over a billion people, I don't know.

Theoretically—or should I say, several of those smart guys who wear glasses and white coats with pens clipped to their top pockets, solve equations, and peer at computer screens say—someday babies could be made from the blood, hair, or skin cells of children, grandmothers, and even deceased people. Can you imagine? It looks like there are very weird possibilities emerging. Do *Frankenstein* and *Jurassic Park* come to mind?

Of course, at this point, I'm wondering, what if we find the DNA of Jesus, and if we did, could we organize the second coming? Wouldn't that be something? Mind you, I don't think anyone has ever found traces of Jesus, not so far, that is. Except for that shroud. Maybe we can lift some genetic material from the blood. People may think, provenance would be an issue for a while, but once the second Christ got going and started performing magic miracles again, everything should be good.

I wonder whether the yellow peril whom the U.S. government has selected as our latest 'enemy number one' will choose to resurrect someone? If they do, look out; that's all I can say.

Something else that just occurred to me. Since some Americans are concerned that a population of over a billion people gives China an advantage rather than a disadvantage over America's global leadership, we could even things up with made-to-order kids, without having to bother the fairer sex. A government department could budget the number required with specific characteristics, and presto: no more equal opportunity issues.

Also, it may solve the immigration problem. That is, why import people when we can make our own? Someone like Trump or Billie Jean King (why Billie Jean, I don't know, her name just popped into my head) would definitely go for this. Of course, I'm joking. Take it from me, I never liked Hitler.

The second area of concern is China itself. During the past 40 years, it seems like it has become a country trying to integrate Communism with Capitalism. So far, the result has been a corrupt, authoritarian dictatorship, tremendous economic growth and a wealth gap or inequality issue almost on par with America. When America and Europe supported China in the race towards opening up its economy, they thought it would eventually lead to the end of communism and the birth of democracy over there.

America and the West were wrong. China is advancing its techno world on its own terms, overseeing closed markets, censorship, and technological theft. But what excites the Chinese government more than anything else in the digital world is population control and surveillance.

We are told that China has the most advanced recognition technology globally, which they use to control their own citizens. Not only that, but they are selling some of these repressive products to other authoritarian regimes throughout the globe. By utilizing Artificial Intelligence, it is reported that almost every adult throughout China has been photographed and graded for such things as political opinions, preferences, and behavior. Also, all phones are compromised, and the location of individuals can be monitored 24 hours a day. It is said that the technology being used can identify a person even if they wear a mask.

If you believe all of that, then I guess Big Brother has arrived.

Of course, we are also told that at this moment, the U.S. has the edge in digital technology, and it's like, "Phew, we are still beating them." This is an American thing; we have to believe we are winning, but then you think, wait a minute, that means…?

So as I reach the end of the road, and given all that has happened in only a short time during my life, I anxiously wonder whether Doreen and I will meet a better world when emerging from isolation?

Asia has risen and is a place where the vast majority of the world's people live. Will their policies triumph? Who knows? We are about to survive a plague, see the back of Trump, and start cleaning up. There's a lot to do and much to be optimistic about as we must now turn our attention towards saving the world from humanity.

The Election's Over

Thank God the election is over, and Trump is out, but the pandemic remains. Anyway, what I am wondering as I type away on the computer, gaining inspiration from a wall and the same bloody squirrels running around outside—should I have tagged them with a paint gun to satisfy my curiosity whether they are the same greedy sods as a year ago? No, not that. What I'm wondering is, what do ex-U.S. presidents do?

Of course, many of them are quite old when they finish their term and also quite exhausted, and I suppose that is only natural after wheeling and dealing with Congress and the rest of the world.

Mind you, I'm not wondering about this outgoing billionaire prima donna. I am quite certain that this soon-to-be-past, son-of-a-bitch president, will be spending a lot of his time figuring out how he will avoid jail, paying hefty fines, and ensuring his wife doesn't clean him out during divorce proceedings. But once again, maybe I'm wrong. Perhaps that's just my wishful thinking.

Coming down off the mountain top, the pinnacle, must mean that anything approaching everyday life is anticlimactic. Speculating on some of the other ex-presidents: deer-in-the-headlights Bush, he watches baseball; Carter builds houses for the poor in out-of-the-way places; but what about the younger blokes like Clinton and Obama, both of whom were around 55 years old when they left office?

Bill Clinton's net worth is around $120 million. He left office when he was 55 and has mooched around ever since—organizing his presidential library, whatever that means, and opening an office in New York City. He also maintains an active speaking schedule. Apparently, he's devoted a lot of his energies to several everyday post-presidential chores: writing a memoir and overseeing the creation of a foundation to combat HIV/AIDS, foster racial and ethnic reconciliation, and promote poor people's economic empowerment. Is it me, or does this sort of thing sound like a shady front for making money?

Clinton has a reputation for being one of the most astute political analysts within the Democratic Party and rakes in over a quarter of a million dollars per speaking engagement. I recently learned that he made approximately 700 speeches from 2001 to 2015. That's about one speech a week for 15 years, and a lot of money. I must say, I'm also thinking, if he was that astute and was being listened to, one wonders after Obama was elected where the Democrats went wrong and why Hilary lost out to Trump.

If I remember right, after his election, Obama made a point of meeting Clinton. They got together for a round of golf, and Clinton peppered him, that is Obama, with opinions and advice on what he should and shouldn't do. Obama got fed up with that and canceled the game halfway through. Maybe for the Democratic Party's sake, Obama should have paid more attention to Clinton.

Then we have Barack Obama himself, whose net worth was $1.3 million in 2008 and today is a hundred times that amount. An increase in wealth of around $129 million in 12 years. Now that takes some doing. We are told it was acquired from a pension, writing books, and speaking engagements. How come, someone may ask? And I would suspect you are unlikely to get a full and proper accounting from either Barack or Bill to a question like that.

Obama pulls down $400,000 per speaking engagement, and he and his wife have supposedly written several books. For his last book, Obama was paid an advance of $65 million. Now I'm thinking, that's serious money. Insiders in the publishing business say that fathoming the math is impossible because the sum paid is, in itself, so far from the norm.

As one rights publishing associate put it: "We're all so blown away by the numbers on this deal that the sky's the limit, right?" She went on, "I've rarely seen seven-figure deals, but these numbers are new to the game."

The Obamas are not holding back; they are going for the gravy train big time. Do they really spend a lot of time thinking and doing for the lower class and Democratic Party's ideals? Unlike Bernie Sanders, Elizabeth Warren, and AOC are the Obamas willing to risk becoming unpopular with the corporate hand that now feeds them? Words are good, but action is better. That's what I'm thinking.

Another thing that you, mister wall, need to tell me is whether it is acceptable for a person, who has just left office as the president of America, to be laying out in some detail what he had just done and experienced while in office.

Before Gerald Ford, ex-presidents lived simple lives and were not expected to make outside income aside from book royalties. Ford changed all that by getting paid to make speeches, appearing at conventions and meetings. He even opened a shopping center and became a member of the board of large corporations in America. And now it appears to me that the Obamas are on a course to eclipse all others as they sign an agreement with Netflix.

So here we are, talk about selling air B&B time in the White House. We've even privatized for profit the president's office.

And what can we expect from an ex-president who has successfully avoided being impeached? *I was right all along; everyone else was to blame.* The ego has no shame. How will Trump be remembered if he escapes jail, the man who gave the rich a trillion dollars and supercharged the Covid-19 pandemic in America?

Hopefully, I'll get out of this here isolation alive and will eventually find out.

In the Wilderness

I was wondering, am I the only one who feels as though life right now is kinda surreal? I don't feel as though I am quite in touch with things. It's not just that, but I don't seem to be able to focus on what day or time it is, or which meal I missed, or whether I should take Jack for a walk.

Everything is passing by. What's real, and if you're not sure of that, what has value? By the way, how can the government suddenly start giving billions and trillions of dollars away? What the hell is negative interest anyway—how does that work?

Do I care if I have all the stuff? Should I become a naked Naga sadhu and smoke pot all day, or a Buddhist? Wait, not a Buddhist, Christ, imagine it: shiny bald head, no socks, and permanent half-smile on my face, along with glasses. Do they wear underpants, they all wear sandals, don't they?

I was also wondering, whether I am the only one who, at night, when climbing into bed, thinks that I only just got up and not much has happened in between? Should I say my prayers? Am I worried that my life is evaporating, that I'm moving towards the invisible?

And the answer is, *yes*.

Talking about evaporation reminds me of my fountain in the garden. I couldn't understand why it was running out of water so quickly during warm and not-so-warm days. I sort of studied it over time, looked and looked for leaks, and found none. I switched the fountain pump off to try and measure the loss, but it turned out to be minimal when static. Of course, I didn't want to admit the obvious, that it was all due to evaporation when the fountain was operating. Simply by having running water, and due to its action having water droplets mix with warm air, it evaporated at an extraordinarily fast rate, almost before my very eyes. I didn't measure it, but it must have been gallons within a few hours. Naturally, I wanted to calculate the loss so that I could take steps to manage it predictably. But I couldn't find a formula that took into account all the specific conditions. So, no garden laboratory experiment there.

Then I got to thinking, evaporation, condensation, we come from water, the cycle of life—jeepers what a thought brought on by my fountain. In this lockdown situation, I feel as though I am aging quickly. Am I evaporating?

Anyway, the thing is, one doesn't always want to accept what is actually happening in front of your eyes because even some of the most mundane events do not appear logical; that is, there had to have been a leak right—wrong.

I suppose that's how it is for other instances in life, and also, the opposite situation most often can be true. Such as, you calculate or have the belief that something has to be true when in fact, it isn't. A psychiatrist may have a fancy name for that condition, or perhaps only water people figure out these things. What are they—hydrologists, meteorologists, dowsers, firefighters, or Trump—I don't know.

Back to the unreal, the phantasmagorical or bizarre; I watched Mike Pompeo on the TV the other day. He's the one I refer to as *melon head*. Pompeo's a big old-boy—big head sticking out, belly sticking out, bum sticking out—you get the idea. And I was wondering, besides eating a lot of hot dogs, what's really going on in his mind? I believe he was top of his class at West Point, went to Harvard Law, and during a short stint as head of the CIA employed his old buddy, his business partner, as head of CIA operations. Can you imagine?

The thing is, I'm thinking how impressive those soldiers are who graduate from the world-renowned West Point Academy. You automatically know what they convey. They seriously look as though they represent honor, morals, honesty, duty to serve, courage, and leadership.

At what point did it all go wrong for melon head? Was it long before he thought it was funny to dispute the authenticity of the democratic presidential election, but never his boss? Of course, I'd previously heard him speak in that dismissive, arrogant, bullying manner that he has. I suppose he's been trained to be someone's or anyone's contemptible bulldog.

Therefore, we need to ignore how disappointed his wife and children and relatives must be as they follow and attach themselves to this man who exhibits such low moral character. But rather, consider how he has besmirched and dragged down the reputation of West Point. That is, down to his level. A man who behaves like a bombastic, then cringing child, obviously fearful of the cheap White House con man. The shyster MAGA man who has gathered around him people of low standing; including those who are totally unqualified for the responsibility they hold. They are the people who are already in jail, should be in jail, or have one foot in jail.

I wonder what Pompeo thinks when he puts on his pajamas at night. Or when he goes to church and communicates with God. I'm hoping that he recognizes what he does and realizes that in most sane people's minds, he is a donkey. A short termer, without conscience, one of those nihilistic sociopaths you hear about. Or, is he unaware of what he is and will continue to teach at Sunday school as though nothing has happened, unswerving in his maniacal evangelical beliefs? A very dangerous hypocrite indeed.

I was also wondering how many more of his sort is West Point churning out. In order to become a professional soldier, perhaps he is precisely what the military wants. Someone who serves only the command structure. Someone who, under command, can ignore democracy, ethics, morality, and the inalienable rights of people. Someone who can assault decency.

"Don't you agree, Jack?"

Jack strolled in a couple of minutes ago. He usually loafs around, stretches out on the rug near my desk, and listens to whatever I have to say with rapt attention. I'm sure Jack understands most of what I'm saying because he never takes his eyes off me. Mind you, it could be he's waiting for another biscuit. Who knows. Anyway, the main point is he hardly ever disagrees with me.

Left Field

Have you noticed how things come out of left field? There is no discernible response from the wall.

Trumpism is one of them; Covid-19 another; and a cop, kneeling on a black guy's neck until he dies another.

I still can't believe that Trump won the election back in 2016, and I later discovered some people that I quite like and thought were normal voted for him.

When growing up, I remember people were defined or polarized by their religion. "Oh, he's a catholic," or "You only have to look at his nose to know he's Jewish." Much later, it became, "You can't trust them; they are Muslims." These discriminating expressions weren't viewed as racial epithets but prejudices. However, as time moved on, they became racist opinions, and black people, in particular, were singled out as inferior. But for a while, it appeared as though we all sailed in the same pond. Got on with life without thinking too much about slavery and all the other terrible things colonists and conquerors got up to.

Quite possibly, it was the Scandinavians, those fearsome Vikings, who got non-discrimination started. My impression is that their women were on an equal footing with men. I mean, they weren't treated like subservient homemakers, and society at large was collectively responsible for their children. Helga wearing a helmet with horns can be a scary sight. And before the Vikings, let's not forget Queen Boadicea and her daughters; she was a nasty sod who gave the Romans some trouble.

So I'm asking myself, when was it that women were relegated to second class and treated as chattel. And I'm beginning to suspect it was around the time that paganism lost its flavor and the current dogmatic religions began to emerge. Perhaps that's when the domination of the feminine sex began to take root and became the norm. All that is changing slowly as women become more educated and the grip of religion on society weakens. But just as important, 'the pill' has provided women with sexual freedom from bondage.

Anyway, much of this attitude towards equality of the sexes changed throughout continental Europe and eventually found its way to Britain, home of the flat cap, fish and chips, and women in pinafores scrubbing the front doorstep.

However the integration of non-white people, especially black people, and the burden of inferiority on their shoulders has not been lifted. They haven't had a magic 'pill' to help them establish equal status. But, bit by bit, it appears as though racism is declining, although as recent times have shown, it still raises its ugly head in some places.

As I sit waiting, or is it wasting away, peering out of the window at industrious squirrels, my thoughts try to observe and take in America, the place that seems to magnify everything.

This place seems to expose its demons every so often. A violent country, one where many believe they can settle accounts with a gun. Where multitudes of people in cities and elsewhere are shot every week, while at the same time the police are scared, people are afraid, street gangsters multiply.

Ironically, this has resulted in everyone buying more guns while the U.S. pontificates to the rest of the world about liberty, freedom, and individual rights.

Most civilized countries would find it difficult to imagine sending kids to school with bulletproof backpacks and having mass shooting school drills along with safety rooms and armed police in attendance.

And now we have a nationwide cause to deal with. That is *Black Lives Matter*—a movement that has traveled beyond U.S. borders, and wouldn't you know, it's come at around the same time as we are also dealing with a worldwide pandemic. Imagine if it was only Covid-19 we had to worry about.

But no, in this perfect American storm, we have the nation split down the middle. Because now you are likely to be defined not only by the color of your skin, but also your political preference. "Oh, don't pay any attention to her; she's a Republican" or "What can you expect from a Democrat?"

Thank goodness it is not all bad. Trump's term in office as president is coming to a close even though he is kicking and screaming with his arms wrapped around the bedpost, desperately hanging on blubbering, "It's a fix! I'm not going!"

Gazing through a window into the silent garden, I wonder, *Will I get my wish and see him behind bars?*

I doubt it. For some reason, there is an element of fear concerning a possible revolt by a broad section of his nincompoop supporters. I say, call their bluff, round them up, take their guns, stick them in jail, kick arse. Democracy has to win.

In the meantime, be that as it may, I expect New York to continue investigating Trump's shady business dealings and tax violations. And that he will most likely be sued by countless women and others who will spring into action once he leaves office.

I'm fully expecting him to be fighting litigation for another 10 years until someone decides his entertainment value has sunk below the Republican skyline, and he's suddenly struck down by a mysterious illness or assisted suicide. All will then breathe a sigh, and I hope to be around when it finally happens.

Are we turning a corner? Who knows, two jabs of vaccine this Spring, and we'll be going out to lunch, the cinema, and feeling free again, or will we? I think I'll be wearing a mask for some time before feeling confident that the danger has passed. We sure as heck can blame China for the virus, but as for the rest, Black Lives Matter, and Trumpism—much of which we have imposed on the rest of the world—we must bear sole and absolute responsibility for that.

Living with Hope

On the eve of the anniversary commemorating John Lennon's murder, I watched a film about planet Earth narrated by Sir David Attenborough. It started with a reminder of the world's frequent extinctions, caused mainly by events such as too many volcanoes erupting at once, asteroids crashing into earth, and worldwide plagues. But the complete and absolute extinction of Earth's life forms never actually happened. As I've mentioned before, some species of plants, animals, insects, and bacteria, much reduced in number, managed to survive.

The film revealed how an extraordinary number of species evolved to live in harmony with their environment. For instance, if the number of a particular animal group grows too large, some died off until their numbers once again become sustainable.

Anyway, the amazingly successful human population is now almost eight, soon to reach ten billion people. It is growing as it always has by taking territory, converting it to man's use, and producing monoculture crops that do not support other life forms except the locust. And in a never-ending campaign to feed ourselves, we keep exploiting the land for agriculture by pushing back tropical forests.

Of course, we all know that this is not good and can't go on, but we do it anyway. So climate change continues, affecting the monsoons that feed much of Asia, and the rains needed for the Midwest and California. To continue this cornucopia, we constantly oversupply food to our supermarkets, keep the lights on, and ourselves warm by burning fossil fuels in ever-increasing amounts, thereby heating the planet with more and more carbon dioxide and methane. Thus, over time we will no longer need to keep ourselves warm due to increasing temperature and will want a lot more air-conditioning even though we know this too will exacerbate climate change.

It is easy to conclude, especially given our current government, that this will lead to our demise. But the film also showed vast farms created by people in Holland. A small country that has now become one of the largest exporters of food. All on land reclaimed from the sea.

As demand has grown, the Dutch have resorted to building multi-layered farms producing food hydroponically and are very strict on recycling water and waste products. Best yet, they didn't have to run off indigenous people to accomplish this. Nearby, Denmark, by the way, is exporting electricity from its wind-powered grid.

Actually, many technologies are emerging which are within our grasp to combat climate change and create a sustainable world for Homo sapiens. It will be expensive, but there is no alternative. The heating of the planet, migration, crop failure, devastating storms, and floods coupled with the tragic loss of most other species will otherwise be the outcome.

The Nobel peace prize awarded to the World Food Bank was in recognition that feeding people stop them from fighting each other. Well-fed people do not need to join terrorist groups. They can stay home and feed their children.

Good hygiene, along with poverty reduction, demonstrably shows that people with health care security, adequate food, and the ability to earn a living tend to produce fewer children. For example, witness Europe, Japan, China, and even sectors of America where the birth rate is low. By comparison, note those places in the U.S. where there is high poverty, and the birth rate is much higher.

Up to this point, we have moved only a tiny step towards slowing our demand for fossil energy and creating a sustainable world. So I imagine, with a science-guided government, we could well envisage the day when it becomes inconceivable to burn fossil fuels, except perhaps, in my Weber grill so that I can enjoy a hamburger. Imagine multilayer farms producing our food, releasing land back to nature's natural processes.

For the optimist, there is hope, but we need a national, even worldwide, effort to complete this mission for everyone's children. We need to elect into office only those brave enough to take us on a journey towards this more pleasant future, lest we turn our blue planet into an unlivable hell. At least that's what comes to my mind as I notice from within this house, looking through its window, that for a few years now, we have not had the usual change of seasons.

Love

"When someone loves you, the way they say your name is different. You just know that your name is safe in their mouth."
— Billy, age 4

"If you want to learn to love better, you should start with a friend who you hate."
— Nikka, age 6

This prolonged forced separation from each other and the familiarity we all had with our neighbors, friends, and relatives is being replaced by small spaces occupying the mind as degenerative granular brainpower begins to take over. It kinda makes you wonder, why do we have this need for each other so much, even though you may have a dog.

After reading this and that and thinking it over for five minutes, I've concluded that it is an emotional factor. The sort of thing we pretend to remove from our so-called logical or objective decision-making process.

Could it be that emotion is what drives most of our actions and beliefs? A human trait that is impossible for artificial intelligence to replicate. I'm thinking the stock market is a good illustration of emotional behavior. For example, regarding most S&P 500 stocks and their major industries, almost all information is known, yet skilled, intelligent investors and traders often make opposing analytical conclusions and decisions. At a certain price, some buy, some sell, the same stock.

Therefore, I ask myself, beyond the numbers and information, what is it that drives a decision one way or another? A gut feeling, a retained memory causing a bias towards or against something? Are you attracted to one but not the other even though they are similar? Why is that?

Without realizing it, we use words of logic and reason to justify how we come to our decisions when making choices on a myriad of responses. But in fact, very few choose to admit the emotional element.

From the very outset, without our awareness, emotions insert themselves into our decision-making. And when that happens, we behave as though there is no other rational choice. In fact, I'm told that to do something other than what our emotions tell us to do is unusual. If we feel it, we do it.

When reasoned logic points out that you should do something you don't want to do, what then? "I'll sleep on it," you say.

Training, however, does assure a certain amount of spontaneity during day-to-day activities. The point of training is that you respond without thinking. It's an automatic response. Although, even after training, if you do think, that in of itself, brings to bear other factors or considerations which then affect the control of your emotions. Subsequently, this then leads you to act. Something like that.

I suppose psychologists have a great time expounding on this subject. After all, it may fit perfectly with their so-called pseudoscience, and let's face it, those psycho healers are going to have a field day when we all start coming out of lockdown.

Information feeds belief. Belief uses conjecture, misinformation, disinformation, facts, assumptions, and needless to say, it is rare to be all-knowing. But we should not forget, we have to be careful about what to believe because one usually has to live by it.

Therefore, irrespective of religion, politics, and old wives' tales, the answer is: Don't get locked into your beliefs, or metaphorically speaking in the bathroom, without a book. That's what I say. Because if you do, all sorts of nasty things can happen. Okay, enough of that because this leads me to what I was thinking about in the first place—love.

Love—a word that is used to signal more than commitment, more than sex, more than friendship. A binding word beyond reason or logic, beyond rationalization. It is a word that stands alone on the summit of all words regarding human connectivity and beauty. It exists without needing further explanation. A word, which when used, is intended to bind for a lifetime.

Essentially, true love means that you have an unwavering, unbreakable, and unparalleled fondness and devotion for a person. It is also defined by an emotional as well as physical connection with them that runs immeasurably deep. And life without your significant other would be practically unthinkable. Is it unique to the human race? Some say not. Swans come to mind.

But it is, without doubt, the ultimate human emotion, as dangerous as it is wonderful. Pure in its existence but without substance, like the soul. It is a word that is overused and abused but always out there for us to embrace, within and beyond control, no matter the circumstance. Even Covid and all of its misery cannot change love.

Vaccinations

As I sit here watching the rain come down, I'm thinking, it's usually snowing at this time of year, and so this must be the effect of climate change. At the same time, I also remember Elvis in the mid-50s when he had his polio vaccine jab on *The Ed Sullivan Show*. The performance intended to demonstrate that if it was safe for Elvis, it was safe for everyone else to have a vaccination.

A New York City black nurse named Sandra Lindsay recently became the first person from the general public to receive the Covid-19 vaccine. That was also symbolic because the pandemic has disproportionately affected the black community, with over three times as many hospitalizations. And almost three times as many deaths, compared to White Americans. Yet, black Americans are more likely to distrust the vaccine.

It is indeed true that the vaccine was developed in a very short space of time, and there may be some concern about its long-term efficacy. But why one subgroup of Americans are more suspicious of it indicates that black people lack the confidence in what the predominantly white, and once oppressive, authorities tell them.

Obviously, with the predominantly far-right and black sections of society not trusting what the authorities tell them, this signals a severe failure of communications and faith in the country's institutions, predominantly by those who have not advanced their education beyond high school.

It is also a fact that, these days, many people are more likely to be persuaded by bad media and conspiracy theorists than by common sense. Quite clearly, in my view, the government and justice department have to clamp down on media outlets and blatant lying to the public.

If we are to unify the country while trying to maintain and not infringe on the principle of freedom of speech, there must be an open discussion on this critical issue of lying. Without truth and the acceptance of facts, and with overwhelming false claims, democracy itself cannot work properly.

For me it is clear that this pandemic is shining a light on the widespread distrust and inequities in America. So one hopes that, at the end of the day, after many lives have been lost and ruined, some good will emerge from this disaster.

Nature is unforgiving; it is giving us a serious wake-up call and we must stop playing around thinking that this planet exists only for us. I don't care what the old testament says; Nature doesn't give a damn whether you are a conservative or progressive, a socialist or capitalist, a Catholic or Muslim, black or white.

The Covid pandemic has moved around the world with lightning speed, and it is obvious that a worldwide coordinated approach to combat this and other pandemics is necessary. As they say, "it is, what it is," and we need to heal and close gaps. I think it is also safe to say all of us only live once, and it is up to us all to make the most of this fact.

America has an opportunity to demonstrate that it really is the ultimate superpower, capable of world leadership. This should be the country's moment. A moment when it can hold its head up high and demonstrate a non-militaristic leadership. But so far, we are not coming anywhere close to achieving such a thing.

An Assault on Democracy, Jan 6th 2021

Within this house, you might say four walls, is where we isolate ourselves from the world outside. There is a TV and the Internet, and I've re-read all the John le Carré and Len Deighton books. I've flipped through magazines giving them "the once-over" and poured over umpteen poetry books but barely remember many of them, while some seem to be beyond my comprehension.

Another thing, during this self-imposed lockdown, Doreen and I engage in a running competition of Banagrams, applying our own, carefully developed rules that enhance the game way beyond other similar pursuits such as Scrabble and cryptic crossword puzzles. So far, I believe we have played more than 300 games since March. Doreen's winning, of course.

Anyway, what I want to point out is that irrespective of games and books, we depend on the media—that is, TV and the Internet—to keep us relatively sane.

So what do we think when we see the storming of the Capital by crowds of mostly white men aged between 25 and 55 years old? This year we've had black marches and riots mainly in response to police violence, and far-right marches for no particular reason I can figure out, and now this.

One noticeable difference from all other recent demonstrations or riots is that the white insurrectionists who attacked the Capital were not gassed, doused by water cannon, maced, or shot at with rubber bullets even though they broke in and forced entry into the offices of the Capital building.

Based on other recent observations of similar experiences, it was obvious that a different standard is being used when dealing with white versus black demonstrators.

There are several opinions about this disparity and the minimal lack of police response during the assault on the Capital. It seems to me that all the reasons dreamed up so far have elements of truth, including racism in the police force and far-right hooligans being embedded within the police departments and national guard.

This was indeed one of the darkest days in American history and for the respect of democracy. It then got me thinking about the fundamental foundational idea that all people are the same and should be treated equally. That then led me to be concerned about this basic assertion when realizing that we know and can easily show that all people are not the same.

Throughout the world, there are large differences between and within populations. In fact, for me, even though I have heard all the reasoning, it is still a mystery why. Especially when you consider the amount of free knowledge floating around, and yet vast sections of the world's populations remain impervious to learning and personal development. For them, the invention of the steam engine is as much an unknown as quantum mechanics.

Let me tell you, growing up at the bottom end of the Welsh valleys in the 1940s and '50s was no school picnic. My education was transferred to my generation old-style. In old school buildings, from blackboard and chalk, well-used textbooks, uncompromising teachers, and corporal punishment. Not so different than my father's time and not so different from what you may find in developing countries today. Yet most of today's scientific understandings and breakthroughs were achieved and developed during the chalk, the printed word, slide rule, and finally, the first IBM computer period.

So the question is, why are many countries in the world who have the same tools at hand as I had, unable to invent anything except what their tribal ancestors produced? Why have they not advanced metallurgy, physics, mathematics, invented the printing press, paper, the light bulb, etc.? If a country in the early middle ages learned something, why didn't a country in, say, Africa or India learn the same thing, even if it were a hundred years later?

In other words, natural demands were similar. So why didn't evolutionary development occur almost in the same way but during the same or different periods? Why didn't the concept of disciplined learning occur everywhere, that is, if we assume we are all very much the same?

Bringing that thought up to the present time, why is a section of America's white population behaving as though their general education never advanced and stagnated into pools of misinformation, ridiculous ideas, and threads of conspiratorial logic dissolving into total ignorance?

How does the most powerful nation advance if it cannot solve this problem whereby we are not all the same. How does the premise of free speech, individual rights, respect of the law, and commitment to democracy through the electoral process work if our schools and universities churn out bozos? How can we be sure that all common values won't be diminished?

What the hell am I talking about stuck inside four walls with a TV? This country is missing a beat as it militarizes its population and isolates itself, and I have to get out of here. Don't you think?

The Virus

It's snowing! Being in this lockdown due to the pandemic, I suppose it doesn't matter. I've given up looking out the window and wonder, If only walls could talk, what would you say?

Will we ever see the end of this virus. It seems just as we get it under control, with our numbers going down and peaks suppressed, back it comes. Is it because we celebrated at Christmas or New Years', or is it because each new variant of the virus, as it mutates, is much more contagious, more readily transmittable?

They've announced that we now have a bunch of vaccines with varying abilities to keep us safe. Since none of these have been around for more than a few months, no one knows the long-term effectiveness or whether they will cause long-term problems. Wouldn't it be interesting to discover that we've given everyone a silver bullet that lets them live to be 200, or drop dead in 10 years? Who knows. Doreen tells me not to be so pessimistic.

Slowly but slowly, the vaccine output from the various manufacturing sites worldwide is desperately trying to make enough vaccines to treat 7.5 billion people. The U.S. is now gearing up to inoculate most of its 330 million people. As a high-risk, first-group member eligible to receive the vaccine, along with everyone else, apparently, I don't have the slightest idea of when or where to go to receive the jab.

Not forgetting the Herculean response and efforts, undertaken by the scientific and health services, by contrast the logistical management of this pandemic by states and the federal government has been shambolic and verging on criminal negligence. Anyway, I came up with a plan for Doreen and me. It's as follows: Wake up at midnight and start looking around for some organization with both the vaccines and an open appointment.

There was only one problem with this strategy: I was competing with the 2,600 other people my age in my town who are all attempting the same thing. Another problem is that I fall asleep at 10:30 pm and don't wake until 9:00 am.

I've stopped watching the news on television because it's both depressing and annoying with all the commercials and its inability to give a correct perspective on things. But my computer has access too, and I'm rather addicted to the New York Times and BBC. It's impressive the little pieces of useful information one can pick up from these news sources. The UK announced that the Astra Zeneca vaccine keeps people from infecting others. Wait, does this mean people inoculated with other vaccines can still infect others? And what about the effectiveness percentages, 95%, 92%, 72%, and less if you only have one shot. This still leaves a huge number who will fall through the cracks. It's 5% of 7.5 billion or 28% in the worse case, leaving between 375 million and over 2.0 billion people in which the virus can continue to mutate. Add to this the number of people who don't believe in vaccinations. They, too, will increase the pool of carriers in which the virus can mutate. Jesus!

Wait, then consider the several 100 million bats flying around happily hosting this virus. A virus just waiting for an opportunity to jump from the bats that have been hung in a market for a hungry mouth somewhere in the world.

All this worrying Covid stuff is a new addition to other recent viruses that have come along trying to destroy humanity. There's Ebola that pops up in various places, then there's that strange virus delivered by mosquitoes that shrinks a baby's head. These two are uncommon, but there is nothing uncommon about malaria, which may survive further and further north as we heat the planet. Will we have tsetse flies and mosquitoes carrying West Nile disease? Why is it called West Nile disease, anyway? Are things worse on the west side? Are there any answers to all of this?

No, I stoically remind myself, the struggle will go on; man versus nature.

Doreen will be home soon, and I'd better do what she's asked me to do. I stretch, get up, and as I stumble towards the kitchen to pour myself another cup of tea, find that my right leg has gone to sleep.

Color

Perhaps it's true we are not all the same, but be that as it may, the assault on the Capital building was an invasion, and what we witnessed was an insurrection, plain and simple. Something I never thought I would see in this country. Once again, the vast intelligence and public protection resources we pay for let us down.

Having watched the angry all-white mob attack the Capital of the United States, I recalled seeing Ruby Bridges 60 years ago. At the tender age of six, this little girl advanced the cause of civil rights when she became the first African American student to integrate into an elementary school in the South. Since then, it has been a long hard fight to uphold equal rights for black people in America. And the fight is by no means over.

Perhaps when Obama was elected twice to serve as president, most of us could be excused for thinking that permanent change related to racism had occurred.

But we now know we were wrong because afterwards, half the country elected into office a Humpty Dumpty president, who is a racist and misogynist. He was leading an almost all-white, all-male Republican Party supporting the propaganda and lies of the far right. That is, those fascist groups who have blossomed throughout the country, especially during Obama's reign. Even as Obama continued to reach across the aisle, the racist genie of the Republican Party had already escaped out of the bottle.

Political leaders representing one-half of the population, including the con man Billy Graham's evangelicals, a large section of whom are from down South, did not want anymore Obamas. They were all prepared to close their eyes and mouths in order to give their baying crowd of supporters a man of incredibly shallow character. Would big old Abe Lincoln, the first Republican president have cheered them on?

Now Trump is sidelined, but unfortunately not the cause. So here I sit, hypothesizing where the country will go from here. Will the rest of the world give long-term credence to the words of an American president? After all, we seem to change commitments every four years.

It all started way back when we broke our first agreements with the Native Americans. Ever since then, that kind of behavior has continued. I first heard the phrase, "every contract is made to be broken," from an American lawyer years ago, and you know what, I believe it. And if you are anyone like Pompeo and his buddies, you don't even bother with that. You just move the goalposts.

However, getting back to the color issue, there is one thing that is certain: You cannot stop a changing tide that's rising, and so those bastards who pose in camouflage with guns and flags are going to have to adjust their way of thinking as demographics change. And those bastards in government who believe it's all right to have a free market that can, at any time, throw the working class into the street by moving jobs to Vietnam and the like, had better start doing some soul searching. They need to realize who they are working for in order to ensure the damage that has been done can be rectified. That's what I think.

Keeping Secrets

The other day, someone on the car radio was talking about Russia gaining access and possibly hijacking America's intelligence. They were claiming that their cyber attacks are so extensive that it was equivalent to an act of war. Also that China was continuing to steal our trade secrets.

Shake a stick; what are we going to do about it, humph humph, poo to the Ruskies, and boohoo to the yellow peril. Both of you are our mortal enemies.

Lately, when eating cornflakes, I've not been talking to Doreen much over breakfast because basically we have said all there is to say during the many years of half a century. But now, in lockdown, there is no one else except the TV offering alternative thoughts and opinions. However, because it is the start of the day, who knows, something may happen that will inspire a new conversation such as, *Did you wash your hands,* or *Whose birthday is it next week,* and *Should I take the garbage out?*

Anyway, it was around this time I began to wonder whether there was an alternative story behind America's current outrage. After all, hasn't America, for a long time, been spying and stealing information from enemies and friends alike? Snowden made everyone aware of this, and for his audacity, he's been on the run ever since. In fact, we have thousands of people peering into computer screens, over a hundred spy satellites, the most advanced snooping technology, and people just about everywhere feeding information back to the CIA and others.

Today, according to what I read, there are 21,000 people employed by the CIA, 40,000 in the NSA, 35,000 in the FBI, and 230,000 working for Homeland Security. Of course, I researched public data to get these numbers; therefore, I wouldn't be surprised if they are greatly understated and don't take into account other departmental offshoots and contractors. So I think we are not spending huge amounts of money on those advanced intelligence-gathering resources without some return and a high level of success. And I won't be the first person to have looked at the Alexa gadget with suspicion.

Just think, maybe all of this U.S. government kerfuffle is just another lark of finger-pointing—*Look what those scurrilous bastards are doing to us now; you can't trust them.* Or could it be that the Russians, Chinese, and, I don't know, the Norwegians, are also saying, *Look what the frigging Americans are doing; two can play at that game!*

Talking about games, is that all it is? Games? When the Russians or Chinese do something, is it only to annoy America, pull the dragon's tail sort of thing? Is it only about us? Do these people have an end game; what's the point? Do they really believe the U.S. will not find out eventually and that there won't be some kind of blowback?

No!

As I glance through the window without taking in the deck, the lawn, and several sparrows checking out the bird feeder, it becomes obvious to me, that this government outrage is for domestic consumption.

Whether you are Russian, Chinese, or Iranian, you know the power of the U.S. and its allies. You know the word *crush*, and we all know that wars are ridiculous because they degenerate into long-lasting, terrorist-based nightmares.

So I sit here and wonder, what is the point? Perhaps the point is for a political enterprise to maintain the interest of its audience. That is, those who voted for you, those who you govern, they need to believe you are doing something vital, like protecting them from evil. And that means you have to have an international agenda; you have to have a bogeyman that you can use to redirect attention from domestic issues. And you have to have a crisis every so often, somewhere. Anywhere.

Mind you, it seems to me, the way things are going, we are running out of candidate dastardly enemy schemes. I think we may have to invent aliens from out of space soon, or some global crisis to maintain the charade and keep people in order.

I wonder, is it possible that because I'm hanging out on my own, it's making me more cynical?

Nah!!

Demographics

The effects of Covid in America are being felt more by minority groups and the poor simply because they have to work in difficult conditions outside the home, and many of them live in cramped housing. With this in mind, and as I recalled watching an angry white mob storming the Capital building, the effect of changing demographics crossed my mind.

Actually, over the years, I have paid some attention to this subject. That is, the movement and growth of the world's population over long periods of time.

Demographics tell humanity's story, explaining a society's past and present behavior, and just like that, in a relatively short space of time, Covid-19 will permanently change behavior patterns in the immediate future. But what about long term?

Scholars predict 8 out of 10 people in the world will live in Asia and Africa. The population of Africa will triple from 1.3 to over 4 billion people, and the population in western Europe will decrease by 100 million. All by the year 2100 when the world's population will be approximately 11 billion people. Crikey, this change involving the resettlement of people will happen within one lifetime from now. Which, in real-world terms, is no time at all. Mind you, it may not happen if the current pandemic has its way.

Of course, the sort of people we saw fighting with police and scaling the Capital's walls, white conservatives and far-right people, know this. I don't mean that they study macroeconomics and its certainties; far from it. No, they sense it. They see the changes as more non-white people share the schools, media, and political stage. It is a tide they cannot stop, and so they rage against it. They want barriers and isolationist policies; they certainly don't want another black president, which is why they have rallied with Trump and the Republican Party. They are nationalists engaging the notion and slogan *Make America Great Again*. Something similar concerning immigration was also the biggest factor prompting British people to leave the EU.

Once more, it is emotion determining action. That is, emotion overcoming reason and truth by those who believe they have lost something and let us face it, from where I sit, I think they are right, they have lost relevance. And that is what Trump was able to tap into.

Over the past 50 years, there is no question that the lower half of America's working society has lost out big time. *Make America Great Again* appears to make no sense. After all, America is, by far, the most dominant country in the world. But for them, the slogan translates into *Make My America Great Again*. Give me back what I think I had.

For quite some time now, we have lived with a gap within society that has become untenable. Of course, blaming minority groups and other countries is the first wave of attack by the rich, but now the mob, the mad-as-hell underbelly of society, have a leader who is saying the real problem is to be found in Washington D.C. itself. The outcome is that now we are in never, never land wherein a leader's lies, cheating, and crimes are ignored by a vast section of American society and most members of the Republican Party. These old-style, mostly male conservatives have also blatantly given up the moral ground and act as a buttress against the inevitable changes demographics will bring.

Like the cure for climate change, the cure for the world's population explosion, and illegal immigration is known. But it is difficult to deal with and requires sacrifice, particularly for the rich, and therefore they scramble, wring their hands, and hope it can be fixed some other way. But then, along comes the pandemic, which has to be overcome; otherwise, a total disaster will be a certainty.

"Isn't that right, Jack?" He opens one eye and wags his tail.

It seems to me that the insurrection that took place has been fomenting for a while, and it has to be put down immediately. Democracy and all it implies have to be preserved no matter what. But having said that, the cause of the deep-lying resentment and anger also has to be confronted.

It is not enough for government to congratulate itself because the economy continues to grow, and the stock market flourishes. For many people, the cost for them is unhappiness and loss of optimism. And let's face it, the pursuit of happiness and optimism are the two aspects of America that are fundamentally required to support the furtherance of our way of life and our identity in the world.

Who is to blame? The media and both political parties are to blame. The media has stoked up resentment and false narratives. The Republican Party is fractured and pursues all and anything they can label as socialist. The Democratic Party has abandoned its base.

But I'm thinking, perhaps due to our obvious, sorry arse miserable response to the Black Lives Matter movement, Trump cult insurrection, and the Covid pandemic, we will come out the other side of all this and set about putting things right. There is a long to-do list, and the first step will be to acknowledge that the country has been going down the wrong road for quite some time.

Is that likely to happen? I won't hold my breath, but getting Trump out of the White House, and vaccinations in our arms will be a good start. In the meantime, more black, brown, women, and Asian people, along with new generations who are socially-minded, will take over government and industry and change America's portrait forever—whether some people like it or not.

Jack has decided to go home; I think it's his way of saying he's heard enough.

Aftermath

Isaac Asimov said, "There is a cult of ignorance in the United States, and there has always been. The strain of anti-intellectualism has been a constant thread winding its way through our political and cultural life, nurtured by the false notion that democracy means that my ignorance is just as good as your knowledge."

Some people, including me, might say that these are times for deep reflection as America, a country always on the move, once more shows it's many sides. During this isolation period, America has the time to look at and beyond itself, be honest and objective, and establish its identity. That is a common identity, not division. A tangible commitment to improving the long-term future of all people. A commitment that appears to be well beyond the thoughts and intentions of politicians such as Mitch McDonnell, Ted Cruz, and Jim Jordan. I won't hold my breath!

Of course, this current trying period could be viewed as a test. Will we get bogged down by self-serving politics? Can the country lead the rest of the world to a better place and towards a better future for generations to come?

Considering the reign of superpowers throughout history, I believe America has only just begun its global dominance and has centuries of responsible leadership ahead. That is, assuming we don't screw things up. Therefore I wonder, where are we now? Have we touched the bottom by getting rid of a demagogue and his cult following? Will Joe, the white-haired old geezer who is about to take over, be up to the task of leading the nation, pick up the mantel of decency, and move the world towards a better, all-inclusive future?

Who knows? I won't live to see it, but I hope my children and grandchildren will. Doreen and I will get our first vaccination tomorrow. We will have survived. Thanks to science. What more can I say?

The Geometry of Politics

For some reason, while sitting here at my desk, I thought about Pythagoras and Isosceles triangles and all that geometry we had to learn as kids. Perhaps I was thinking about geometry or trigonometry because it occurred to me that we have to move the point of society, make measured connections, balance equations, and close the gaps in order to move forward.

Unless the country is in a state of war or a pandemic, which is the case right now, it is the condition of a domestic economy that governs political attention. And, for those of us who may not be paying attention to what's going on over the long term, it is the influence of changing demographics. Well, at least, that's what I'm thinking.

These days, we have a name for all sorts of groups or trends, but we tend to talk in terms of generations during normal conversation. Even though it varies case by case. A generation averages about 25 years from the birth of a parent to the birth of a child. However, social scientists label age groups by observing behavior patterns, such as Baby Boomers born between 1946 and 1964, Generation X born between 1965 and 1980, Millennials born between 1981 and 1996, and Generation Z born 1997 or thereafter.

Each of these groups has grown up in a different environment—economic, education, employment, technological, and familial situations—which ultimately influences how they see the past and future, and eventually vote.

For instance, we have what's called the Millennial generation, those that were born between 1981 and 1996. This puts them in the current age group of 24 and 39, which represents a subset of the population who have left college or completed an apprenticeship of some kind, have a family, and reached their competence level in their chosen career or lifestyle. The Millennials account for about 58% of the electorate, and only a small number of them claim to be conservative. Compared to the majority of Baby Boomers, that is those born between 1946 and 1964, the majority of Millennials prefer big government and believe that immigrants strengthen the country; and on foreign policy they believe in good diplomacy rather than military strength. Also, they believe in universal health care and higher public spending and that the current system unfairly favors powerful interests.

There are approximately 90 million members of Gen Z (or "Gen Zers") who are more racially and ethnically diverse than any previous generation. They are on track to be the most well educated group yet. They are also digital natives and have little or no memory of the world as it existed before smartphones. Surveys found that similar to Millennials, Gen Zers are progressive and pro-government. Most of them see the country's growing racial and ethnic diversity as a good thing, and they are less likely than older generations to see the United States as superior to other nations.

A look at how Gen Z voters viewed the Trump presidency provides further insight into their political beliefs. The research found that three-quarters of them disapproved while at the same time, only 32% of Millennial voters approved of Trump. Obviously, this leads me to believe that unless there is a major turnaround in the Republican Party's attitude, the political and economic implications are clear.

I ask myself, what drove the younger electorate to the middle and left of politics? Was it the expansion of college education, the increasing gap between rich and poor, climate change, lack of universal health coverage, social empathy? Sat here, still in my pajamas, by the way, looking out of the window, I'm thinking, it could be all of that and similar issues that have pushed the Millennials and Gen Zers left.

So here I am wondering, what was it that prompted this shift in a country that promoted capitalism as the panacea? And, I thought I would go back not to the days of Reagan and all the deregulation idiocy that followed, but to something more familiar only 12 years ago. When the Millennials were in the age range of 12 and 27 years old.

The gap between rich and poor in America had been growing for some time, but somehow people were unaware of the real impact because they were managing to cope. They could borrow against their house, get college loans, and the overall financial demise on their lives was not noticeable. Because of that, a drastic change in opinions and beliefs did not happen.

Then came the American housing crisis, followed by a worldwide financial crisis. And the misguided economic solution chosen with its insidious effect over time.

Now I'm thinking, well, I've got to this point of the argument, though tedious as it may be, I might as well keep going.

Back in 2008, when we voted into office Obama, a guy who was a bit naive as he faced a completely obstructive Republican Party, the country had its financial meltdown. Bernanke, the Fed chairman, needed to act, and he introduced something called Quantitative Easing. Some called it "cash for trash." That was done by exchanging old bad loans with new money underpinned by negative interest rates. By the way, the rationale of negative interest rates continues to escape me.

Anyway, to my way of thinking, free money was being made available to cancel bad loans. The sort of thing we had accused Banana Republics of doing in the past. The result of this was asset prices soared and increased the wealth gap between the poor and the rich. That is, those who depend on wages for their income versus those who depend on rents and dividends and who pay fewer taxes.

Unfortunately, as we were about to discover, once you go down that road of one versus the other, it plays out over generations. It penalizes the young and subsidies the old because when asset prices rise much faster than wages, the average person falls further behind.

This situation then threatens a social contract baked into the American psyche. That is, *all boats rise.* The notion being the faster the economy grows, the better off everyone should become.

As an example of what has been happening, (and is still going on) hourly earnings in America have risen by 22% over the past nine years while the stock market has boomed and property prices rose 34% in Boston, in Houston 55%, in Los Angeles 67%, and San Francisco 96%. Young people are being locked out. Optimism has diminished, and Millennials, etc., have been left a smaller stake in the society they are supposed to build.

Similar developments have taken place in the UK. Interestingly, in the election before the last one, when the UK Labor Party fielded an inept team, if only the vote of those under 25 were counted, the Conservative Party would have lost every parliamentary seat.

So what have we got here in the U.S.? A new president approaching 80 years old who was first elected to a political office 50 years ago. A man who is supported by the younger generation, minorities, and women.

Did the American election follow a similar pattern as the past? That is, the electorate voted for the person they disliked the least. That is, it was a negative vote, against someone, not for someone? Will Biden be able to withstand the hammering he will get during the next four or even eight years? We will have to wait and see.

In the meantime, Trump has defined the Republican Party so narrowly around the priorities and preferences of his core groups—multi-millionaire tax dodgers, older, non-urban, non-college-educated, and evangelical white people—you have to wonder whether the Republican Party will return to some form of normalcy any time soon.

Freedom

Hallelujah, Doreen and I had our second vaccine on March 15th. The next day we felt lousy. But now we're feeling fine, and in two weeks, I'll be able to break free—stop talking to you in here, mingle with the family again, and hang out with friends and neighbors, albeit under somewhat restrictive conditions. That is, for a while, when confined indoors with other people—in a train, car, plane, bus, or places like conference rooms—I think I'll continue to wear a mask and maintain a distance.

Actually, I'm hoping that one day we will all look back and be asking, *What happened to 2020? Where did it go?*—the year that never was—and sometimes ask the question, *Where were you when the Covid panic button was pushed?*

From this desk, facing this wall and window, I think that although 2020 was a disastrous year, it may have also been one of enlightenment. The Coronavirus stormed out of China and attacked the rest of the world; however, unlike previous plagues, this time mankind was far from helpless.

Yes, we had more than enough deaths and serious illnesses, and we still do, but nothing like those levels suffered in the past, such as during the Black Death. It's also a fact that more recently, in 1918, when influenza struck, the virus could not be identified, and a vaccine was never developed.

However, this time, just over 100 years later, when the Covid-19 alarm bell began sounding in December 2019, within a month, the virus was not only isolated but its genome sequenced, and twelve months later, several vaccines were in mass production. This, by all past measures, was a remarkable achievement. It meant that amidst the misery, severe restrictions, political missteps, and isolation worldwide, we were able to see a light at the end of the tunnel especially in advanced countries.

Not only that but, as distinct from the past, crisis management had the benefit of information technology, which made digital surveillance possible such that 'track and trace' made selective lockdowns more viable.

Scientific and engineering advances were also experienced in other areas such as food, which until fairly recently heavily relied on manual labor for output. But now, in the U.S. and other advanced countries, it only requires a small number of people to work on farms. That is, mechanization and technology have dramatically reduced the chance of famine.

For example, during the period of the Black Death, a farmhand harvested about 5 bushels of wheat per day; now a GPS-guided combine harvests 30,000 bushels in one day. In the past, getting food to market involved many people, ships, and other modes of transport. Today one container ship can carry 200,000 tons with a crew of only 22. By comparison, the English Merchant fleet in the middle ages had a total capacity of 68,000 tons and required 16,000 sailors.

Due to these changes and developments, the result has been that while international tourism has plummeted, maritime trade has hardly declined, keeping the transfer of Covid through international travel to a minimum.

Another thing: During this isolation, people like me have swarmed the Internet, which has proven to be a lifesaver for some as they manage to exist in two worlds— the real and virtual. Under these circumstances, I cannot imagine what life would be like without the Internet.

In the meantime, there is no doubt this pandemic has sounded a wake-up call for scientists and politicians in particular. The politicians are the ones who ultimately allocate the money to ensure that science can continue to map out pathogens throughout the world, that resources are made available for research and organizations who monitor and respond to a health crisis, and it has been clearly demonstrated to them that pandemics need an immediate rapid global response.

There should be no more dithering, such as who gets protective gear, whether to isolate or test and trace. It has also shown the management of a pandemic needs less direct interference from idiot politicians, such as Trump. Unfortunately, led by him, the country exposed the ignorance that exists throughout large pockets of American society. In fact, this has become a real eye-opener, and whether we will ever fix it seems rather doubtful.

I would say we have come a long way since the Spanish Flu, and we've shown that we can fight these ongoing battles with Nature. However, unfortunately, mass stupidity, lies, and conspiracy theories may be a sign of a more complicated man-made type of pandemic. That is, the sort society have now are the sort that scientists cannot solve.

Who knows, it's a never-ending circus. All I know is that Doreen and I needed our vaccinations to eventually get out of this house, drive, ride a train, fly in a plane to someplace, any place, and to hell with the rest of it.

Meanwhile, the best we can hope for is that the Republican Party returns to a place of sanity and that Biden drinks his cup of cocoa before going to bed every night.

Where Are We Now?

During isolation, we have nowhere to turn to but the media. Years ago, the media, or should I say, general public information, usually in the form of news, could be found in newspapers, on posters, and on the radio. Then it became newspapers, radio, and television. Then it became newspapers, radio, television, and the Internet.

On the Internet, you can obtain information of a public nature through social media platforms such as Facebook, Twitter, Instagram. But, unfortunately, far-right conspiracy platforms such as QAnon have also had an impact on people. They capture the imagination of the young and vulnerable with outlandish theories and lies, many of which are espoused by some of our politicians, military personnel, police officers, and other responsible public figures.

During the second world war, both sides used propaganda to persuade their target populations that they were the good guys and the other side was evil. This, then continued without interruption during the Cold War. And so bright people cut their teeth on media warfare utilizing limited outlets.

Now the public is overwhelmed, entertained, and brainwashed constantly through all the accumulated means of communication 24 hours a day through various mechanisms, from smartwatches to printed paper, from the virtual to reality. It is the age of communication.

For almost every story or opinion, there is a counterpoint, which takes me back to truth. Where is truth?

In my lifetime, we have gone from word of mouth and airwaves to digital. Older people are almost cut off from understanding, appreciating, and maneuvering the modern digital world, while, for the younger generation, that's all they know; but, has life become more complicated? Yes. Is there a chasm between generations? Yes. Are the younger generation better off? Perhaps. Are people any happier? No. Does the future look safer? No.

So, sitting here, I wonder, will this pause in the West's frantic escalating activity, which has resulted in everyday life being put on hold, change our values? Will people ask different questions and look for a deeper meaning in life? Will anyone notice?

Where's Jack? I need to go for a walk.

Being Accountable

Who are we? I'm sat here mulling over Biden's recent decision not to publicly blame and penalize the crown prince, Mohammed bin Salman, regarding the brutal and blatant murder of *The Washington Post* journalist, Jamal Khashoggi.

The administration imposed economic sanctions on a number of Saudi citizens connected to the murder plot and issued visa restrictions on 76 individuals believed to have threatened dissidents abroad. Whatever all that means, and whatever good that will do in practice. But so far we have not called out the main perpetrator.

We are told the new administration is concerned that doing so could jeopardize the relationship between the U.S. and a key Middle East ally.

Someone, probably a pompous Nelly from Georgetown, wrote that punishing the crown prince would cause more harm than good. Why? Because, he would say, Saudi Arabia, plays a crucial role in advancing America's interests in the Middle East, including the push to halt Iran's nuclear ambitions, stifle terrorism, and promote stability throughout the region.

I believe someone else, probably a pontificating so-called arrogant State Department strategist, said that angering the crown prince would undermine those pursuits and may force the Saudis to seek alliances with rivals of the U.S., such as China and Russia. Also, they may say that any hopes that the U.S. might help Saudi Arabia to one day become a more equitable nation that can transition away from its reliance on its oil reserves depends on an amicable relationship with the crown prince.

And I say, what a load of tosh. You've got to be kidding me. Here we have one of the most oppressive and backward regimes in the world who, for some time, hosted citizens that financed al-Qaeda, and those who carried out 9/11, and I suspect helped finance ISIS. Saudi Arabia is a country whose only real significance is that it sits on a lot of oil—an energy source that foreigners discovered and exploited, while the local hierarchy loafed around and was bought off. Local sheiks rely on expatriate labor and know-how to keep the country running while they languish in idleness and govern by meting out medieval punishment using harsh semi-religious laws. Penalties such as public whipping, beheading, chopping off hands, stoning, and enslaving women.

Other than supplying oil, I have to wonder what vital role do these people play. After all, ever since both Bushes decided to wave a big stick, the Middle East has been in flames resulting in death, famine, and destruction. So it doesn't appear to me that amnesia diplomacy has worked very well. Not only that, but the world is awash with oil as renewable energy resources continue to grow. So, the chances are that the U.S., except for its military supply business, will have less and less need to maintain a blindfold relationship with the Saudis.

As for Iran and its nuclear weapons problem, the impact or connectivity with Saudi Arabia escapes me, plus the opinion that we need them to stifle terrorism; now that's a laugh. What was the other one? Oh yes, Saudi may go off and seek an alliance with China or Russia? It seems to me that the last thing the Saudi princes want is a bunch of revolutionary communists and desperate oligarchs banging around. No, the reality is they depend on the U.S. to defend them and for their existence.

While playing from a hand that is getting weaker every year the Saudi's need to cut deals. So, for the country to become more acceptable, the royal family should be told what they have to do to shape up. If this recent decision to let the crown prince off the hook is an example of our new government's use of diplomacy, then I think they are way off base.

Although, when you weigh it all up, perhaps it is in character with America's foreign relations policies. It seems to me that ever since World War II, the U.S. has willingly abandoned its ideals when they have become economically or politically inconvenient.

I'm of the view that hypocrisy has prevailed ever since the Cold War started. Perhaps it has always existed. Perhaps all countries behave in the same way, and America is not exceptional. Oh, oh, no one is going to want to hear that. During all that time and until now, we have been prepared to bring down governments across the world in order to impose any and all tinpot crooked dictators who claimed they opposed communism.

On our doorstep, Central and South America are perfect examples. A place where we preferred to support tyrants and murderers rather than the oppressed because the oppressed in desperation may turn to socialism and organize labor, and that would never do. So what has been the result? Broken economies, rampant crime, and people running away.

We took the same approach in the Middle East, supporting the Shah, Hussein, Assad, and Diem in Vietnam before it all got out of hand.

People used to complain that the Trump team ignored diplomacy when dealing with other nations.

Well, as I sit here thinking about the sort of mess we have become embroiled in from Korea, Vietnam, Iraq, 9/11, Iraq, Afghanistan, Syria, Cuba, and Saudi Arabia, not to mention poor Yemen, then I have to say that so far, our type of diplomacy has not done very well. On the other hand, rushing into war has not achieved much either, except accounting for many deaths, destroyed lives, debts, and frightening military capability.

It seems that over time, America will always keep old friends, make new friends, lose friends, and get them back again. But our global commitment to truth, justice, and human rights protection should remain crystal clear and obvious for all occasions, not be reduced to transactional compromise.

I guess some will say I'm naive, but if the nation doesn't honor and maintain its principles, who are we to criticize others? Moreover, why should our people on the front lines, including journalists, depend on the protection and support of their country when it plays fast and loose with its founding principles while criticizing the likes of Putin, Xi, and Kim Jong-un?

In fact, with this Biden message, and the latest issue being his refusal to make public the 9/11 report, I have to wonder, who are we protecting? And, although I know we had to get rid of Trump, I have to ask, who is the real Joe Biden with a wayward son? Is the old dodderer leading or being led?

Clock Is Ticking

The Homo sapiens have always been the cleverest of species. Once we got down from the trees and stopped worrying about food storage and covering ourselves to ward off the cold, we moved on to all sorts of ventures. And as I sit here, I wonder why we spend so much money and effort inventing ways to destroy ourselves, or counting how many angels are on the head of a pin and other useless enterprises.

There are two clocks keeping time for us. One is known as the Doomsday clock. It reputes to signal the amount of time before midnight of our wiping out the planet with our arsenals of nuclear weapons and the lack of action to reduce climate change. The furthest the clock has been set back was 17 minutes to midnight in 1991 after the collapse of the Soviet Union and the signing of the Strategic Arms Reduction Treaty. Then, in 2020, the clock moved the closest it has ever been: 100 seconds to midnight. What? Did it say one hundred seconds!!?

Is this startling fact a topic of investigation and concern placed high on the public's need-to-know agenda? I suppose there's not much you and I can do about this. However, it is unsettling to know that our governments, and that of China and Russia, are still investing in faster and more destructive systems to ensure our so-called defense. This of course, moves the clock relentlessly forward. Tick. Tock.

It makes no sense. No one in their right mind would start this catastrophe, I hope. Yet still, we build. What is the point? If a country uses its arsenal, nothing will be left. So wouldn't it seem reasonable to stop making things worse by increasing the risk?

We have put massive surveillance systems in space, supposedly to avoid being caught out by a surprise attack. Now, countries are figuring out how to neutralize these systems. And so the cat-and-mouse game continues. Imagine a blinded world, with its systems suddenly shut down. I can see it now, generals rushing in screaming, *We must attack!* Boom! The end of civilization just as the clock strikes midnight.

There is another clock: the Metronome, a climate clock in Union Square, tells us how long we have left to fix climate change before it becomes irreversible. The last I checked, it was 219 days, one hour, six minutes, and two seconds. Yikes, is it true? We are about to find out. Anyway, it turns out that roughly 100 companies are responsible for more than half of the pollution that negatively affects climate change. They are companies supported by government subsidies and investment from financial institutions that hold them in their portfolio.

The two clocks tick away, illuminating an existential problem that we need the world's very best minds and leaders to sit down calmly and address. Or we could be forced to follow Elon Musk to Mars and attempt to start again in his climate-controlled radiation-blocking habitats. No, thank you, I like my world.

So I find myself wondering why so many intelligent people are fooling around with string theory and multi-universes and concepts of multiple dimensions when we have some serious problems to solve here, in our four dimensions, right here on Earth.

There are other perfectly intelligent people who are dedicated to perpetuating the idea that an almighty power created a perfectly designed universe and is in control of everything. Therefore climate change isn't something to worry about; it's just the natural phases of the planet. They have other odd ideas, such as all life began 5,000 or 6,000 thousand years ago despite the vast troves of fossils and other data that clearly show that this is not correct.

If some believe in the Divine being, which is their God-given right, they should just remember we are supposed to be good stewards of the land, and the Lord helps those who help themselves. We haven't been doing much of either recently.

Most of the problem-solving we are doing seems a waste of talent. I listened to a discussion on "what is consciousness" the other day. It was very intellectual, but I thought, what was the point? They should have been addressing our real live dilemma of how we keep going as a civilization.

One thing we know is that the cost of dealing with disasters caused by ever-increasing climate catastrophes is much more expensive than what's needed to fix climate change. Imagine trying to move Miami and New York and other coastal cities up into the Appalachian mountains.

Finally, we have this pandemic, and I'm stuck here talking to a wall worrying about things I can't fix and learning that the virus keeps mutating and maybe, the mutation from South Africa will not be stopped by our vaccine. I think I've made myself depressed again. Will I ever get to take Doreen to a fancy restaurant or the theater? Who knows.

Moving On

I don't know whether I'll be talking to you anymore. It seems life may be getting back to what I would call *normal*. Doreen and I are elated because finally, we were able to hug our children and grandchildren, and let me tell you, it was a wonderful experience.

It is coming to the end of this conversation, the wailing to a wall, as I plan our escape into the blue beyond. Towards people and conversation, and I look forward to the herd effect kicking in.

This will be the gradual removal of masks and gloves, the free movement of people, the planning for events and holidays, and booster shots before the next scare comes barreling in. Hopefully, it won't be a virus, and I will not be sharing my thoughts with you while in isolation.

Instead, I'll be with real people, hanging out hypothesizing this and that, annoying some, and entertaining others.

Perhaps now we will all put our shoulder to the wheel and tackle climate change solutions before the clock runs down and our human species as we know it, ceases to exist. But for this precious moment, all I can say is that it looks as though Doreen and I dodged another bullet.

Now it is time for me to get off my bum and enter the new world with my gardening tools, writing book cynical attitude, and leave the past 17 months behind. Of course, we won't be going to places like India or any other country outside the Western world any time soon. Unfortunately, those less advanced countries still have a long way to go and possibly millions of deaths to go before any indication of normality returns to them.

And now I'm wondering, as we pick up the pieces, who, in ten or one hundred years time will history blame for this Corona ordeal.

The Final Word

Here I am, sat at the window, back talking to you. We are gradually coming out of our isolation and have greeted the real world. A world that feels a little strange, with more cars on the road all seeming to be traveling too fast. Some shops are boarded-up, some closed. This was war without the bombs. Is it over? Am I a different person, a better person? It's too early to tell.

One thing I can say is that I feel as if I've aged five or more years not the 18 months since the isolation thing kicked in. My reflexes are much slower, muscle strength much weaker, and enthusiasm much dimmed, and I don't think it's because I am over a year older.

No, I think it is the lack of social comfort, purpose, connection, inspiration, and sharing. The unknown energy we feed off people. My thought is that it will never fully return. Something was lost. And maybe that is what I have been talking to you about. Recognizing, without realizing it during all this time. That is the bond developed throughout the network of humanity, linking each of us to others. A bonding that evolved perhaps genetically through the ages ever since humans first organized social groups has been interrupted. And that, I suspect, is what has been lost. At least for the moment.

I am sure most of us can now begin to understand the mind-bending issues a person who has been in solitary confinement goes through. For us, in reality, it was not absolute isolation; nonetheless, I'm assuming because it was over such a long period, the impact will leave scars.

Let's face it; here I am still returning to this room and having a conversation with a wall. A temporary force of habit, I suppose. Perhaps returning to normalcy is still some ways off as Doreen and I begin to hang out with a few people, usually without our masks on, but we still have to be reminded what day it is.

When will normal visitations to doctors and dentists begin to take place is uncertain, and joining thousands of people at public events is some ways off for Doreen and me.

I also notice we are not talking about planning long trips or vacations. It seems as though we are in a wait-and-see mode.

Then there are the grandkids, most of whom are returning to school. Will we ever know what effect this lost year and more has had on them.

I just learned that Biden warned Putin: That if Navalny dies in prison, America will make sure there are serious consequences for Russia. It sounds to me like Biden has been drawn into making an empty threat. There is no one more supportive of squeezing Putin than me. But, going back to what I mentioned a couple of months ago—where was Biden's condemnation of the Saudi mob after they murdered Kashoogi?

It seems we are up for a fight with countries like Russia and China that can resist and trade blows with us. That is, if you believe half of what both parties claim. But we are not ready to bash a so-called friendly country's leader who blatantly murders critics and dissenters. I just don't get it. But there it is; I live in a country that embraces hypocrisy.

"Doreen, I tell you what, let's go out for lunch and visit the library. Hooray."

The Madhouse

I'm back. I didn't mean to, but here I am with one more thing to add, and no it's not going to be about the Delta Virus. My thinking is that vaccinations will deal with this over time.

No, this is about the irony of this-and-that, which doesn't really register until you have plenty of time to think or reminisce. Such as when you are, or have been in some state of isolation. It is then that you start to question everything. And that is where I am now. I find that one of those questionable aspects of behavior that I may have previously mentioned and often ignored, is hypocrisy. Especially national hypocrisy.

Beliefs, actions, and sins of the past get buried during the rewriting of a country's history, and we re-parcel the truth because we don't want to be seen as murderers, torturers, slave traders, and the type of people who benefit from disgrace.

Over many years society has evolved, and we have got rid of most monarchies, brutal dictatorships, and psychopathic leaders. Or so we think. Now we measure our behavior against a set of humane principles, individual rights, and just laws. Not a crown. Or so we think.

In this regard, Americans like to believe that they are at the forefront of advanced civilized behavior, promoting opportunity and equality for all. And that was my general impression for a long time until now.

Now I have had time to reflect and accept that everything in America gravitates towards and from politics. Politics drives everything, and today's media has thrust this untidy democratic system of our government onto the general public, blasting away on an hourly, daily basis. Who said we need to know the what, where, why, and when every second, somewhere in the country and across the world. And the why, you as an individual, should be concerned or in some way remotely affected.

Not only that, but we are constantly being asked to take a position; make your opinion known, which then serves to polarize and quickly generates A versus B.

Quite recently, what I found interesting was that one of the world's most informed, fiscally conservative, and highly regarded newspapers, *The Financial Times*, finally had enough of the Republican Party/Trump nonsense.

Now, I have been taking *The Financial Times* newspaper for over 40 years, and my view is that overall, it is one of the most balanced papers in the UK and quite possibly the Western world. It is read by most senior business decision-makers, high net worth consumers, influential policymakers, just about everyone in the English-speaking finance industry, and people like me. Politically, it is strongly aligned with the Tory party, which I suppose we could say is somewhat empathetic with the Republican Party, with its editorial stance centering on economic liberalism, notably free trade and free markets. And so you can imagine my concern when I read their recent editorial, which did not hold back or pull any punches concerning the current state of the Republican Party. I'll read it out loud:

"There are so many dysfunctional policies being implemented that the destruction of America's fiscal position goes almost unnoticed. Any claim the Republican Party might once have had as a guardian of budgetary probity lies decades in the past. Trump and congress, instead of keeping campaign promises, has cut taxes that benefit the rich. Trump also showed another familiar

Republican behavior, i.e., playing brinkmanship and threatening to close the federal government. For some time, a broad pattern has been clear—a Republican Congress or Republican president worsens the long-term U.S. fiscal position before Democrats are elected and set about repairing it. Paul Ryan is not a fiscal policy wonk as has been touted. His plans for combining tax cuts with control of the deficit only added up by assuming unrealistic growth rates and unspecified improbable spending cuts."

When considering the source, this is as damning as it gets for the Republican Party. If the GOP cannot win over the voice of finance and capitalism, what the hell are they doing?

It worries me because, as I have mentioned before, given the current trajectory, demographics favor the Democrats by a long way. Unfortunately, the Republican Party has engaged itself in hyperbole, lies, and mismanagement, currying the favor of the very rich and stirring up the lunatic fringes of America without any viable economic blueprint. And this is a problem.

The country needs at least two strong political parties to govern a strong democracy and republic effectively. We need the checks and balances based on principles and facts, not mob insanity and the likes of the Coke brothers financing disruption. When *The Financial Times* throws its hands up in despair, the Republican Party needs to take heed, do a reset and bring serious people to the table.

The country is groping its way out of the pandemic, and I'm leaving isolation with a little trepidation and this is the time when we all need to come together. We have a climate crisis just around the corner that sounds ominous, and let's face it, this will take all the energy and cooperation available throughout the world, especially in America.

In the meantime, for now, I'm fed up with talking about all of this. So, I think I'll have a cup of tea and take Jack for a walk.

America: What's All That About?

There was nothing unusual about that particular Tuesday. Ron had flown in from Cairo and landed at Heathrow Airport two days before and he was now paying a visit to the cemetery on a hill overlooking the town in which he was born. A cemetery where he could find most of his parents' relatives.

"Hi, Dad it's me Ron," he said, "come to put some flowers on your grave." He picked up the flower pot. "I won't be a minute."

Offering a greeting to a grave was not unusual. Some people would also quietly and briefly share with their past loved ones a favorite prayer or poem, some people even sang. One man read the newspaper to his dead wife twice a week. Loss is a terrible burden.

It was as though there was a coming together of those past and present, an acknowledgement of everlasting love, faith, and perhaps the spirit of the Holy Ghost.

He returned from the fountain with a pot full of fresh water, arranged the flowers, removed a few twigs and brown leaves from the grass mound, touched the top of the headstone and then, *bang*!

Almost immediately, and to his astonishment, a thought flashed through his head. Ron instantaneously took a step back and stood for a moment with a perplexed look on his face.

He warily leaned forward again, put one hand on the stone and then quickly pulled it away.

"Jesus, it spoke. Wow!"

Rags, Cats, and Bones

The cart's wooden, steel-rimmed wheels wobbled and rumbled along until finally stopping near their house.

"Whoa boy, whoa," shouted the man.

Gwyn and his sister hopped from one foot to another in excited anticipation while tightly holding worn sweaters, pants, and various rags. They had also convinced their mother to part with an old iron poker and a rusted tin bath with holes in it. They knew the Rag and Bone Man would want the metal. He was always asking for metal.

Years ago, people like him also collected bones which they sold to chemical works for making glue. There was a glue factory in a tough, lower-working class area, off Corporation Road, a couple of miles away from where Gwyn lived. When the factory was boiling bones, a horrible stench would invade Gwyn's part of town. It was sickening. Years later, Gwyn imagined that it was how places like Auschwitz must have smelled.

Living with Hope

Stan nonchalantly folded one leg over the other, leaned back slightly, and with a half smile locked eyes with Larry.

"Listen, I already told you, I'm busy. Why don't you give your name and phone number to Brutus here, along with the reason you want to speak to me and I'll see what I can do." Larry had made an indication towards the big tough-looking guy.

The two girls giggled.

They were in the Parisian one of two nightclubs Larry owned. It was just after ten o'clock and the place was warming up. Larry looked as if he was already into something.

Stan Hope uncrossed his legs and leaned forward. "I'm Chief Inspector Hope," he said casually, still with a look of amusement on his face. He turned and nodded towards the two girls. "Why don't you two girls go somewhere else before I decide to check-up on your age, work visa, and whatever else."

They both turned to Larry with a surprised 'what do I do' look. He waved them off and patted one on the butt as they started to move away towards the dance floor.

Stan pointed at the girl with a ring in her nose. "On your way, ask someone to bring me a Coke. Make sure it's unopened. They can open it here in front of me."

"What do you want?" Larry asked.

Let's wait for my Coke before we get down to it.

****

"Do you like vegetables, Larry. You know carrots, cabbage, that sort of thing?"

"They're all right. Why do you ask?"

"Do you like flowers?"

"Flowers?"

"Uh, huh, flowers."

"What is this, why are you asking me these stupid questions?"

"Ah, hang on, here comes my Coke." Stan put two pound on the tray and said, "Keep the change."

The waitress nervously looked at Larry who, with a wave of his hand and a smarmy smile said, "Put your money away. It's on the house. That's the least we can do for an important officer of the law such as yourself."

"I tell you what Larry, just so you have this straight, unlike some who call themselves policemen and have been known to frequent your establishments socially, a number of whom you may know, I pay my own way. And I'll also have you know that two pounds for a glass of Coke is extortionate but we'll leave it like that. Another thing, if and when I take you down to the station one of these days, I want you to know our cups of tea are free."

Ginger Biscuits

These memoirs tell the events of my history since I first hitched a ride on my families time line. It is a compendium of stories that originated in an industrial Welsh town, took me to London and then dropped me off in America. From there I travelled the world—Europe, South America, North and South Africa, Indonesia. I left my mark in China and was almost killed in Sri Lanka and Cairo. At the same time, I have insured that the Dowden name emanating from my grandfather in 1874 will continue through his three great great grandsons.

Life Came to Me

A first book of poems

Revelation

A second book of poems

Made in the USA
Middletown, DE
27 November 2021